IT WORKS LIKE THIS

IT WORKS LIKE THIS

A
Collection
of Machines
from
nature and science
Magazine

EDITED BY THOMAS G. AYLESWORTH
DOUBLEDAY & COMPANY, INC.
GARDEN CITY, NEW YORK

CONTENTS

INTRODUCTION

How many times have you gone to the basement to change a blown-out fuse? How often have you had to replace a defective ball in a toilet or a worn-out washer in a dripping faucet? Did you ever take a clock apart to see what makes it tick, only to end up with a tickless clock? When was the last time the power lawnmower broke down and you wondered how to go about making it work again?

You probably have watched repairmen fixing your washer, your refrigerator, your television set, or your family car and wondered how these men were able to perform miracles in applied technology. The explanation is simple—the basis of their skill is that they know how these devices work. Without an understanding of how machines work, the repairmen could never discover what is wrong.

NATURE AND SCIENCE, the Natural History Press's science magazine for young readers, has for several years published articles explaining how some of our more common tools and machines operate. Call these things devices, call them gimmicks, instruments, implements, utensils, gizmos, apparatuses, trappings, or whatever you want, here are some of the best descriptive articles written by the editors of NATURE AND SCIENCE—designed to help answer the question, "How Does It Work?"

Thomas G. Aylesworth

APPLIANCES

A lot of programs have been broadcast since the idea of television was developed in the early 1930s, and the first commercial stations appeared in 1941. Although mothers and fathers are now complaining that their children spend too much time glued to the set, there was a period when a television set in the home made a person as popular as if he owned a swimming pool. But after all these years, few people know how the TV set works.

TELEVISION

Suppose a machine gun is fired while being swung from side to side. The bullets hit the ground in a line, kicking up dust which hangs in the air for a while. Inside your television set, a different kind of rapid-fire gun kicks up puffs of light in a pattern of lines that makes the picture you see. This gun shoots out *electrons,* tiny particles that are in all kinds of matter.

When you turn on a television set, a hot wire at the narrow end of the *picture tube (see Diagram 1)* starts shooting a fine stream of electrons at the *screen,* or front of the tube. The inside of the screen is coated with a substance called *phosphor* that glows when electrons strike it.

A stream of electrons is an electric current, and an electric current can be pulled by a magnet. There are electromagnets at the neck of the tube. The pull of each magnet keeps changing, so the electron beam is pulled in different directions. First it strikes the screen in the upper left corner (*see diagram*), then moves across the screen, leaving a line of light glowing wherever the electrons hit. From the right side of the tube the beam jumps back to the left side and traces another line just below the first one. This keeps on until the beam reaches the bottom right corner of the screen, then it jumps back up to the top left corner to repeat the same pattern. Each trip of the beam over the entire surface of the screen is called a *scan,* and each scan happens so fast that your eye sees all the light on the screen at the same time.

When many electrons are flowing through the beam in a second, the spots where they hit the screen glow very brightly. Where the screen is dark, fewer or no electrons are hitting it.

Meanwhile, in the Television Studio . . .

The number of electrons being fired at any instant is controlled by signals from a television camera (*see Diagram 2*). The light from an object in front of the camera strikes a plate (instead of a photographic film) in the camera. This plate is *light-sensitive,* which means that if light hits a spot on the plate, the light knocks electrons out of the plate at that spot. Where the light is bright, many electrons are knocked out of the plate; where it is dark, few or no electrons are knocked out.

From the back of the *camera tube,* a hot wire shoots a beam of electrons that scans the plate. When the beam strikes a bright part of the plate (where light has knocked many electrons out), electrons in the beam enter the plate and stay there. But when the beam hits a dark spot, the electrons already in the plate push the electrons in the beam away from the plate. These beam electrons travel to a *collecting plate* which sends them out through wires as electric current. This changing current makes the signals that reach your television antenna and control the flow of electrons in the picture tube of your set. Where the televised object is bright, your screen becomes bright; where the object is dark, your screen is dark.

Color TV

White light and all other colors of light can be made by mixing red, green, and blue light in different ways. A color television camera separates the light from the object into red, green, and

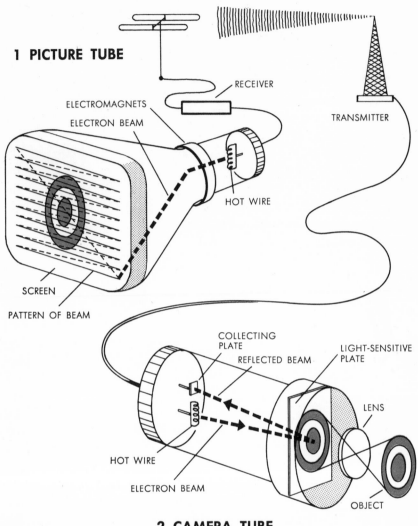

1 PICTURE TUBE

RECEIVER

ELECTROMAGNETS

ELECTRON BEAM

TRANSMITTER

HOT WIRE

SCREEN

PATTERN OF BEAM

COLLECTING PLATE

REFLECTED BEAM

LIGHT-SENSITIVE PLATE

LENS

HOT WIRE

ELECTRON BEAM

OBJECT

2 CAMERA TUBE

blue light, and the camera sends out a different set of signals for each of these colors.

In a color television receiver, the inside of the picture tube screen is covered with tiny dots of three different kinds of phosphor. Some dots glow red, some blue, and some green when they are struck by electrons. There are three electron guns in the tube; one shoots electrons only at the dots that glow red, another at the dots that glow green, and so on.

The dots of light are so tiny that your eye can only see groups óf them. Where a group of red and green dots is glowing on the screen, you see a spot of yellow light. Where a group of dots of all three colors are glowing, you see a spot of white light.

The late 1880s were noisy times. Thomas Edison, Alexander Graham Bell, and at least two other lesser-known inventors were working on the development of record players. Since that time, there have been so many improvements made on this device—stereophonic records, long-playing records, tweeters, woofers, and so forth, that using a record player in the home may be even better than going to a concert. But the machine itself is still merely an example of applied physics.

RECORD PLAYER

How does a record player get sound out of the grooves in a record? Actually, there is only one long groove on each side of the record. The groove spirals in from the edge toward the center of the disc. If you look at the record through a strong magnifying lens, you can see that the walls of the groove are wavy (*see Diagram 1*). The size, shape, and arrangement of these waves in the groove walls make the different sounds that you hear.

When you put a record on the turntable of a record player and turn the switch to "on," an electric motor makes the turntable and the record go around at just the right speed. When you set the needle on the record, the needle rides along in the groove as the record turns. The wavy walls of the groove make the needle move rapidly from side to side. The needle moves back and forth faster to make a high-pitched sound than it does to make a low-pitched sound.

As the needle moves back and forth, the top end of it pushes against a small piece of crystal. Each time this crystal is squeezed, it sends out a tiny current of electricity. The current gets stronger or weaker as the needle pushes against the crystal or moves away from it.

This electric current flows through wires to the *amplifier*. There the current is *amplified,* or made stronger, by passing through electronic tubes or through transistors. When it comes out, the current is still changing its strength many times a second, as it was when it came from the crystal. Next, the current goes through wires to the *speaker,* where it is turned into sound waves.

How the Speaker Works

In the speaker there is an *electromagnet.* This is a wire coiled around an iron core that becomes a magnet when electricity flows through the coil. Near the electromagnet is a permanent magnet (*see Diagram 2*). If you hold two magnets close to each other in a certain way, you can feel the magnetism pushing the two magnets away from each other. This is what happens in the speaker. Each time the current going through the coil gets stronger, the electro-magnet gets a "push" away from the other magnet. This makes it vibrate, or move back and forth, as many times each second as the current changes its strength.

The electromagnet is attached to a metal *diaphragm* that is in the center of a *cone* made of stiff paper. The diaphragm and the cone vibrate along with the electromagnet. As they vibrate, they squeeze the air in the speaker and form sound waves. The sound waves make your eardrums vibrate the same number of times each second as the needle is vibrating in the record groove, and you hear sound.

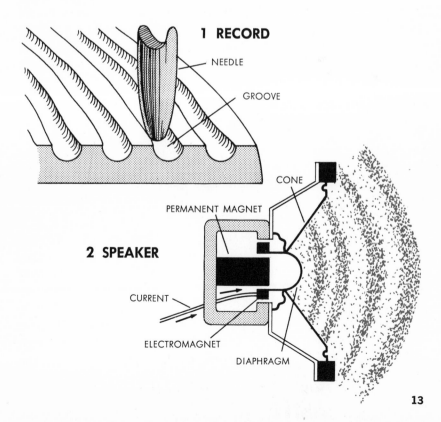

1 RECORD

NEEDLE

GROOVE

CONE

PERMANENT MAGNET

2 SPEAKER

CURRENT

ELECTROMAGNET

DIAPHRAGM

What could be more natural than a desire to hear ourselves speak, since we're all in love with the sound of our own voices? But the early home recorders were massive machines that made non-erasable discs, and almost required an engineer to run them. Then came instruments that recorded on wire. These could be erased, but the wire often broke. It wasn't until magnetic tape was developed that a really practical home recorder was available.

TAPE RECORDER

A tape recorder turns the sound of your voice into a magnetic code on a strip of tape that you can store and play back whenever you wish. Each time, your voice and words will sound exactly the same. Here is how it works.

When you switch on the recorder, the tape begins to unwind from one reel and onto the other (*see Diagram 1*). This tape is a ribbon of plastic, usually ¼-inch wide, that has tiny particles of iron spread in a film on one side. (On a fresh tape, the particles point all different ways.)

Between the reels, the tape passes over the *recording head,* which is connected by wires to the *microphone.* As you speak into the microphone, your voice makes sound waves in the air that

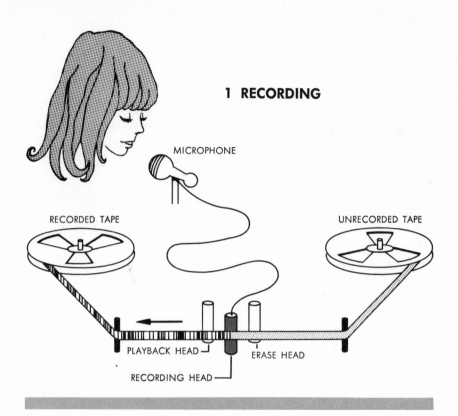

1 RECORDING

MICROPHONE

RECORDED TAPE

UNRECORDED TAPE

PLAYBACK HEAD

ERASE HEAD

RECORDING HEAD

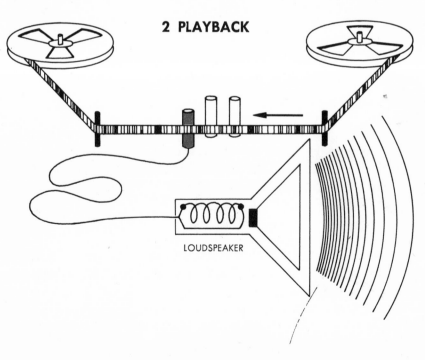

2 PLAYBACK

LOUDSPEAKER

push a thin metal plate, or *diaphragm,* back and forth in the microphone. When the diaphragm is pushed inward, more electric current flows through the microphone than when the diaphragm moves. outward. A loud sound makes more current flow than a faint sound, because the waves made by a loud sound push the diaphragm farther than the waves made by a faint sound. A high-pitched sound moves the diaphragm in and out faster than a low-pitched sound, so a high sound changes the flow of current more times per second than a low sound.

The current made by the sound waves flows from the microphone through a wire coil in the recording head, making the coil an *electromagnet.* As the tape moves across it, the electromagnet pulls on the iron particles and makes some of them line up in the same direction, so that they form magnetic spots on the tape. (The same thing happens to the particles of iron in a nail when you stroke it with a magnet.) A strong pull from the electromagnet (loud sound) makes strong magnets on the tape. A weak pull (faint sound) makes weak tape magnets. A rapidly changing pull (from high-pitched sound) gives the particles that are close together different magnetic strengths. A slowly changing pull (from low-pitched sound) makes the strengths of the little magnets change more gradually along the tape (*see Diagram 1*).

To turn this magnetic record of your voice back into sounds, you press a button that disconnects the recording head and connects the *playback head (see Diagram 2).* The playback head also contains a wire coil. When a magnet is moved around near a wire coil, it makes an electric current flow in the wire. This is what happens as the magnetic spots on the tape move past the coil in the playback head. And the harder a magnetic spot on the tape pulls, the more current flows in the coil.

This constantly changing current is then *amplified,* or strengthened, and fed into the *loudspeaker.* There the current goes through the coil of another electromagnet, which pulls a piece of iron back and forth each time the current changes its flow. The iron is attached to the center of a stiff paper cone, called the *diaphragm.* The diaphragm pushes the air in and out, making sound waves just like those you sent into the microphone.

To erase sound from a tape, you turn on the erasing head. The current in its wire coil keeps changing so fast that the iron particles on the tape are scrambled up again.

Even television signals can now be recorded on magnetic tape and played back through a TV set to reproduce the original picture as well as the sound.

During the American Civil War, the Northern army cut off the Confederates' supply of ice. But the Southerners were able to get a few new cooling machines from France. So we have had mechanical refrigeration in this country for over 100 years. Even so, except in cities, the ice cube was a rare sight until the 1930s. Now, however, almost everyone has electricity in his home, and the ice wagon has gone the way of the steam automobile.

REFRIGERATOR

Pour a little rubbing alcohol on the back of your hand and feel what happens. One thing you notice is that your hand feels cold. Another thing—the alcohol *evaporates,* or changes from a liquid to a gas, very quickly, leaving your hand dry as well as cool. To change from a liquid to a gas, heat is needed. The heat comes from your skin. Evaporation is a cooling process, because it uses up heat.

Ancient peoples learned to cool water in pottery jars by allowing some of the liquid to seep through the sides and evaporate. By this action the water inside lost some of its heat. Today, campers some-

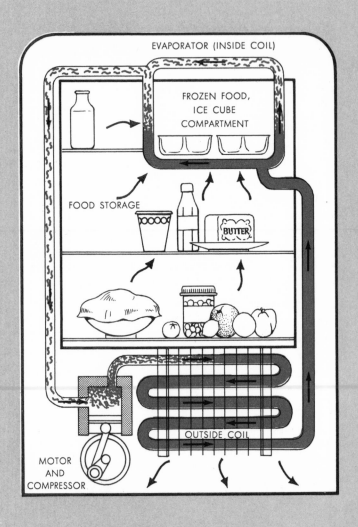

EVAPORATOR (INSIDE COIL)

FROZEN FOOD,
ICE CUBE
COMPARTMENT

FOOD STORAGE

BUTTER

OUTSIDE COIL

MOTOR
AND
COMPRESSOR

times hang food up in wet cloths to keep it cool by evaporation. A camper's canvas water bag cools water by seepage and evaporation.

The refrigerator in your kitchen works very much the same way. But it does not use alcohol or water as a *coolant*. Instead, it uses a manufactured coolant called *freon*, which can exist as a gas or a liquid. Let's trace the freon as it makes one round trip through the refrigerator.

Liquid freon is forced into the evaporator, a coil of tubing that surrounds the ice cube compartment (*see diagram*). As the liquid freon changes to a gas, it draws heat from the air in the refrigerator. The air, in turn, draws heat from the food in the refrigerator. The gas now flows from this coil to a *compressor*. The compressor is a pump, driven by an electric motor. It squeezes the gas into a small space so that it becomes a liquid, or *condenses*.

As the freon condenses, it moves through an outside coil, where the liquid gives up its heat. The heat is carried away from this coil by room air circulating through it. If you place your hand on the outside coil of your refrigerator, it will feel warm. (This coil is in the bottom of some refrigerators and on the back of others.) Next, the liquid flows from the outside coil back into the evaporator coil, where it changes into a gas.

This process happens over and over again. The coolant evaporates and condenses many times each day. But you have probably noticed that your refrigerator does not operate all the time. You can find out how often the electric motor turns on and how long it runs each time. Listen to the humming noise it makes, and time these events.

Refrigerators Are Also Heat Pumps

Refrigerators take heat from the food inside and release the heat outside, where it heats the air in the kitchen. So they are heaters as well as coolers. Any machine that transfers heat this way is a *heat pump*.

A home air conditioner is another heat pump and operates much like a refrigerator. Air from the inside of the house is pulled around a coil in the air conditioner by an electric fan. A coolant evaporates in the coil, taking heat from the inside air, which is then blown back into the room. The coolant then condenses in a second coil, where it gives off heat to the outside air.

A home deep freezer is simply a very cold refrigerator. While your refrigerator keeps the temperature of the air inside between 40° and 45° F., a deep freezer keeps it about 0° F. A control dial permits you to set the refrigerator to the desired temperature.

We have been a lot more comfortable since Willis Carrier developed air conditioning in the early 1900s. We don't have to blow air over cakes of ice any more, and we seldom suffer in a movie theater (at least from being overheated). Air conditioning has come so far during this century that it is possible to cool off 66,000 people in one room—for example, in the Houston Astrodome at a boxing match.

AIR CONDITIONER

You get the "shivers" when you come out of the water at a beach or pool because your skin suddenly gets colder than it was when you were in the water. A thin film of water is left on your skin. This water is *evaporating*—changing from a liquid to a gas called water vapor. To go through this change water has to be heated. In this case, the heat comes from your skin and leaves you feeling cold.

Air conditioners evaporate a liquid to cool the air in a room. A liquid *refrigerant* in the air conditioner moves from a container through a valve into the *cooling coil* (*see diagram*). The valve controls the amount of refrigerant flowing into the coil.

After the liquid moves into the coil it evaporates quickly, and the gas that is formed spreads through the coil. As the liquid evaporates it takes heat from the metal forming the coil, thus cooling it. A fan draws air from the room into the conditioner, where the air loses heat to the coil. Pushed back into the room, this air picks up heat from your skin, so you feel cool.

Next, a pump removes the refrigerant gas from the cooling coil and *compresses,* or squeezes, it into a smaller space. This warms the gas. From the compressor the gas travels into a coiled tube called the *condenser coil,* which is exposed to the air outdoors. Even though the outdoor air may be 95° to 100° F., it takes heat

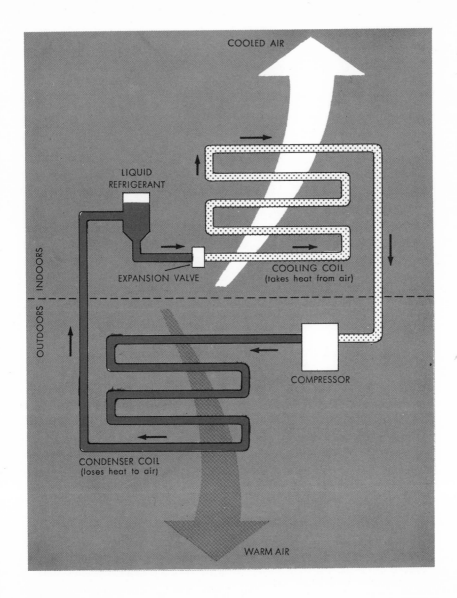

COOLED AIR

LIQUID
REFRIGERANT

EXPANSION VALVE

COOLING COIL
(takes heat from air)

OUTDOORS | INDOORS

COMPRESSOR

CONDENSER COIL
(loses heat to air)

WARM AIR

from the coil because the compressed gas inside is hotter than the outside air. As the gas gives up some of its heat, it condenses, or turns back into a liquid. The slightly cooled liquid now flows back into the storage container.

Like a refrigerator, an air conditioner is a *heat pump*, which takes heat from one place and moves it to another.

On a hot, humid day, when the air contains a lot of water vapor, an air conditioner helps dry the air. Some of the water vapor condenses on the outside of the cooling coil and is drained off as liquid water.

Here's an old timer. The sewing machine goes back to 1830 in France and 1846 in the United States. Even before the advent of the home electrical system, almost every house contained a sewing machine operated by a treadle mechanism that was powered by the sewer's feet.

SEWING MACHINE

Sewing by hand is a slow process. It takes even longer if you want to make *lockstitches,* like this:

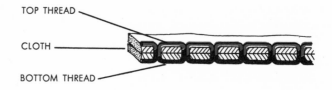

A sewing machine can make as many as 2,200 lockstitches a minute! Here is how it works.

The *top thread* (brown) comes from a spool on top of the machine. It runs through the *needle thread tension* (which keeps

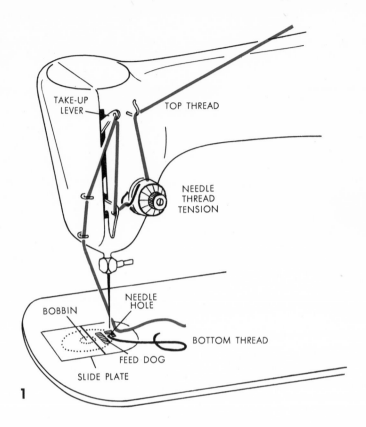

the thread at the proper tightness), then through the *take-up lever,* and down through the eye of the needle, which is near the point (*see Diagram 1*).

The *bottom thread* (black) comes from a small spool called the *bobbin,* which rests in the *bobbin case* under the *slide plate.* How do the two threads get together to make a lockstitch?

First, the threaded needle goes down through the cloth and into the needle hole. When the needle reaches its lowest point in the hole, the brown thread is caught by the *hook* in a collar that turns around the bobbin case (*see Diagram 2A*). As the collar turns, it pulls a loop of the brown thread over and under the bobbin case (*see Diagram 2B*). When the hook nears the needle hole again, the brown thread is pulled upward by the take-up lever. This lifts the brown thread out of the hook and tightens the loop it has just made around the black thread, forming a single lockstitch (*see Diagram 2C*).

By this time, the needle has lifted out of the cloth, and the *feed dog* (*see Diagram 1*) has pushed the cloth a short distance so it is ready for the next stitch.

An electric motor inside the sewing machine moves the needle and take-up lever up and down, turns the hook collar, and moves the feed dog back and forth. The motor is switched on and off with a foot pedal or a lever operated by the sewer's knee.

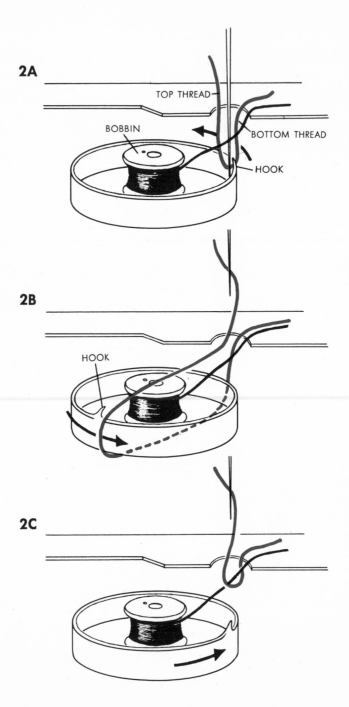

The first motor-driven vacuum cleaner was put on the market in 1899. But several decades later, small boys were still hanging rugs over the clothesline and hitting them with rug beaters to knock out the dirt. Spring cleaning used to be a real chore. However, the time came when the electrical system was installed and the vacuum cleaner arrived in the home to stay. Rugs have been cleaner and small boys happier ever since.

VACUUM CLEANER

Have you ever wondered how a vacuum cleaner picks up dust and dirt? Some vacuum cleaners are tanks with a hose attached to one end. The other end of the hose is a metal pipe with an opening where the dirt is picked up.

Another type, called an upright cleaner, has an opening under the front of the motor case, and a large cloth bag attached to the handle. Whatever the shape, all vacuum cleaners work just about the same way.

Here is a way you can see how a vacuum cleaner works. Lay a piece of paper about the size of a postage stamp in the palm of your hand. Then hold one end of a soda straw about a quarter of an inch above the paper and draw air from the other end of the straw with your mouth.

Drawing air out of the straw leaves a "shortage" of air, or *partial vacuum,* inside the straw. This means that the air pressure in the

25

straw is lower than that of the air around the bottom of the straw. Air outside rushes into the straw to equalize the pressure, carrying the piece of paper with it.

Dust from a carpet is pushed into a vacuum cleaner in the same way. Inside the tank or motor case there is an electric fan. When the motor is switched on, the whirling fan blades push air out the back end of the cleaner, leaving a partial vacuum in the hose. Air around the pick-up vent is at normal pressure. It rushes in, carrying dust from the floor or carpet with it.

In a tank-type cleaner, this air passes into a removable cloth bag on its way to the fan. Dust particles can't get through the openings between threads that make up the bag, so they are trapped inside the bag. But the air goes right through the bag and out the back end of the sweeper.

In an upright cleaner, the fan is close to the pick-up vent. It pushes air and dust into a large cloth bag which traps the dust particles but lets the air escape through the cloth.

Cloth bags for both cleaners can be emptied and used over and over again. Paper bags through which air—but not dirt—will pass are often used inside the cloth bag. The paper bags can be thrown away after they have been used.

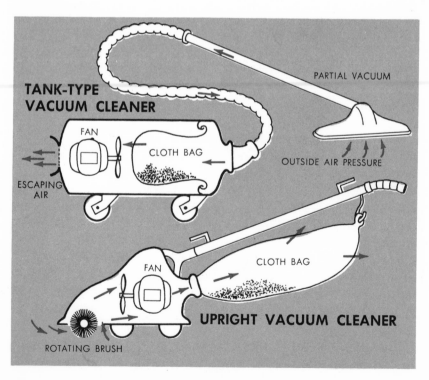

In the 1770s, housewives used a simple plunger and a tub—that was a washing machine. Even when the first electric machines were developed, washing was still a full-day's job. The clothes were washed, then run through a wringer, then rinsed, then run through a wringer, then rinsed, then run through a wringer again, and someone had to be on duty almost all of the time to change the water and keep things from getting tangled up. But with today's washers, the key word is automatic.

WASHING MACHINE

An automatic washing machine seems to be doing many different things as it washes and rinses your clothes, then spins most of the water out of them. But during the half hour or so it takes to launder your clothes, only four *different* things happen inside the washer.

The four different "happenings," or *operations,* are these: 1. Water flows into the washing tank. 2. A cylinder inside the washing tank turns slowly, tumbling the clothes about in the water. (In a machine that you load from the top, the clothes are stirred by a center post that turns back and forth.) 3. Water drains out of the washer. 4. The cylinder spins rapidly to throw water out of the clothes.

Some of these operations take longer than others, and sometimes several are going on at the same time. Each operation is started or stopped by a switch in the *timer* unit (*see diagram*), which programs the "happenings."

How the Timer Directs the Operations

When you press the starter switch (or push a quarter into a coin-operated washer), an electric current starts the *timing motor*. This motor is something like an electric clock motor, and it turns a long shaft very slowly. On the shaft are four *cams,* or discs with squared-

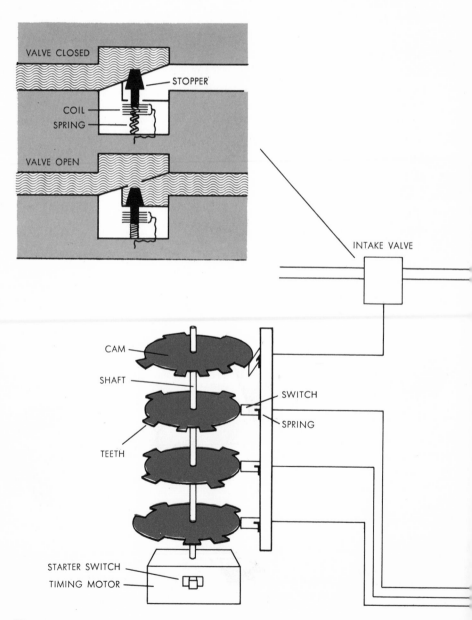

off "teeth" spaced unevenly around their edges. Beside each cam is a switch that controls one of the machine's four operations.

As the cams begin to turn, a tooth on the first cam pushes down the switch beneath the cam, sending an electric current through a wire coil in the *intake valve* (*see diagram*). The current makes the wire coil an electromagnet, and it pulls the metal valve *stopper* into the coil, opening the valve to let water into the washer.

When the cam tooth has turned past the switch, a spring pushes the switch up, stopping the flow of current through the wire coil. Since the coil is no longer pulling on the stopper, a spring pushes the stopper back into the valve opening, closing off the flow of water.

Then the second cam switches on the *drive motor* at slow speed, and a belt that is pulled by the motor turns the tumbling cylinder just fast enough to keep the clothes moving around in the water. After a few minutes, the second cam releases the slow-speed motor switch, and the third cam pushes down the high-speed motor switch. At the same time, the fourth cam opens the drain valve, so that the soapy water can drain out of the machine as it flies out of the rapidly spinning clothes.

The timer then puts the machine through the same series of operations (though timed differently than before) to rinse the clothes and get them ready for drying.

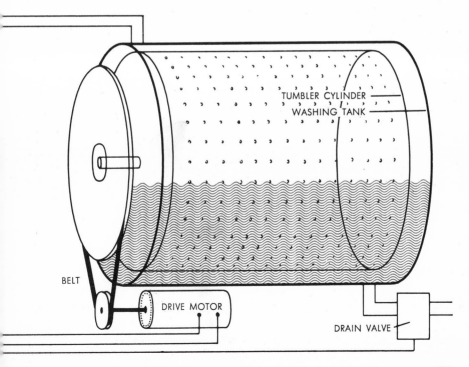

TUMBLER CYLINDER

WASHING TANK

BELT

DRIVE MOTOR

DRAIN VALVE

Otis developed the first elevator in 1852, and Larson invented his push-button improvements in 1922. But it wasn't until the power blackout on the Eastern seaboard in 1965 that many people realized how important the elevator is to them. Imagine having to deliver the mail to the top of the Empire State Building without an elevator.

AUTOMATIC ELEVATOR

An elevator is raised and lowered by an electric motor that turns a grooved wheel, or *drive sheave,* at the top of the elevator shaft. Steel cables run from the top of the car up the shaft, over the sheave, and down the back of the shaft to the *counterweight.* The counterweight balances the car and its load, so the motor does not have to lift all of the car's weight. The downward pull of the car and the counterweight keeps the cables pressed tightly against the sheave so they will move when the sheave turns. The car and counterweight have *roller guides* that run along the *guide rails* on the walls of the shaft.

To use the elevator, passengers press the up and down buttons at each floor landing or the numbered buttons inside the car. The landing and car buttons are connected by wires to the *selector* and *controller* at the top of the shaft. These electrical units act as a kind of computer that "remembers" all passenger calls and controls the movements of the elevator until the calls are answered.

As the elevator moves up in the shaft, it stops automatically when it reaches each floor where a passenger has pressed the up button or for which someone has pressed the button in the car. When the elevator has answered the highest call, it automatically reverses and then stops at the floors where people have pressed the down buttons.

A cable attached to the side of the car turns the *speed governor* at the top of the shaft (*see diagram*). If the governor turns too rapidly, its "arms" spread outward and throw a safety switch that sets the brake on the drive sheave. If this brake fails to stop the car's rapid drop, the governor grips the *governor cable.* This makes *safety clamps* on the car spring out and wedge against the guide rails, bringing the car to a slow stop.

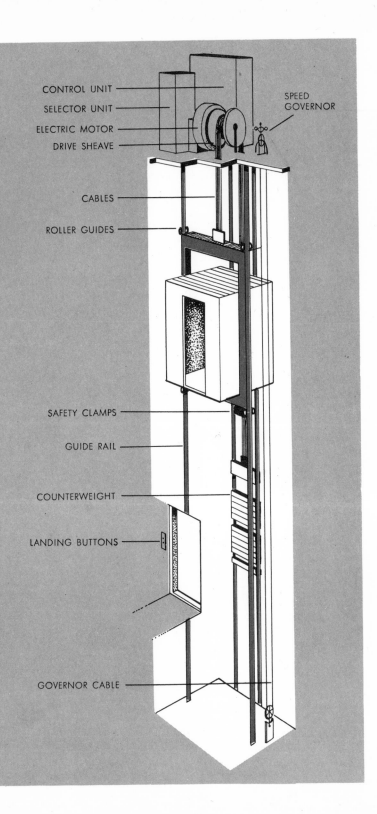

CONTROL UNIT

SELECTOR UNIT

ELECTRIC MOTOR

DRIVE SHEAVE

SPEED
GOVERNOR

CABLES

ROLLER GUIDES

SAFETY CLAMPS

GUIDE RAIL

COUNTERWEIGHT

LANDING BUTTONS

GOVERNOR CABLE

AROUND THE HOME

Spray cans are filled with many different things—paint, whipped cream, insect repellent, and shaving cream, to name a few. Oddly enough, there is a relationship between the spray can and the refrigerator and the air conditioner. They all depend on a substance that will easily change from a gas to a liquid. Often this substance is a chemical such as freon.

SPRAY CAN

Have you ever wondered how a spray can works? If you ever dropped a bottle of soda pop, then took off the cap as soon as you picked up the bottle, you saw the principle of the spray can at work. To make the pop sparkling and bubbly, carbon dioxide gas is blown into the bottle before it is sealed. The gas is packed so tightly in the bottle that some of it pushes out into the air as soon as you remove the cap. When you drop or shake an unopened bottle, the gas that fills the space at the top of the bottle gets mixed up with the liquid. Then, if you take off the cap, the gas rushes out and takes some of the liquid along with it.

Spray cans work on the same principle. Along with paint or some other liquid, a gas is forced into the can at a greater pressure

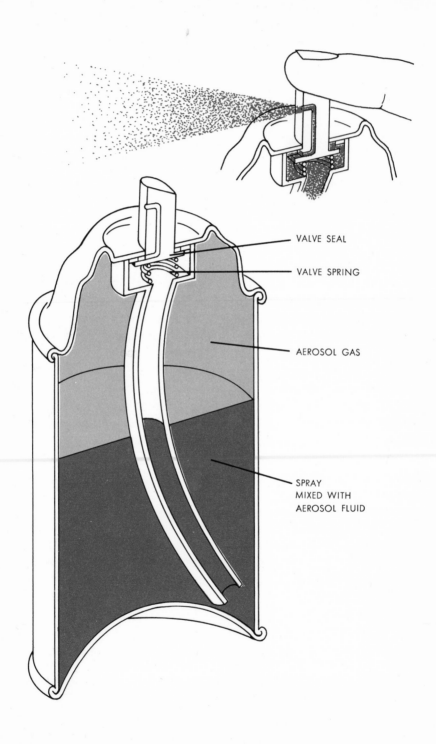

VALVE SEAL

VALVE SPRING

AEROSOL GAS

SPRAY
MIXED WITH
AEROSOL FLUID

than the air outside and the can is then sealed. When you push down on the valve, a passage opens, and some of the compressed gas escapes through a tiny hole in the valve head. This escaping gas forces some liquid out with it as a spray. A spray of tiny liquid droplets is called an *aerosol,* and spray cans are often called aerosol cans.

When spray cans were first invented, compressed air was used inside the can. These spray cans did not work too well because the compressed air lost its pressure quickly and would be all used up while there was still liquid in the can. Engineers tried to solve this problem by sealing the air in the can under very high pressure. Then, however, extra strong cans were needed to keep the pressure from exploding the cans.

Eventually, engineers solved this problem by using chemicals like freon, a substance that changes easily from a gas to a liquid. Freon is a gas when it is kept at normal temperature and air pressure, but it becomes a liquid when it is compressed to about six times normal air pressure.

Fluids like compressed freon are now mixed with the paints and other liquids that are put in spray cans. When the valve on top of the can is pushed down, the pressure inside forces out some paint and some freon. As soon as the liquid freon meets the lower pressure of the outside air at the opening of the spray can, it becomes a gas and pushes the paint out in a fine spray.

The diagram on page 34 shows a cutaway view of a spray can. The spring at the base of the valve keeps the valve closed and helps seal the high-pressure liquids inside the can. The bottom of the spray can is curved inward so that it can withstand the outward force of the compressed liquids inside. Such high pressure might push out the bottom of an ordinary flat-bottom can.

Spray cans should always be kept away from fire and other heat sources. When it is heated freon changes from a liquid to a gas. If that happens, the pressure inside the can increases and there is danger of an explosion.

For hundreds of years, men used either a piece of stiff grass, called a reed, or a long feather, called a quill, to write with ink. Then in 1884, Waterman developed the first fountain pen, and schoolboys and schoolgirls all over the land were freed from the dismal chore of sharpening old-fashioned pens. Of course there are cynics who say that teachers immediately began giving out longer homework assignments.

FOUNTAIN PEN

The tip of a reed or quill was once sharpened to a fine point to produce thin lines, or to a broader point to produce thicker lines. In both cases, the point was split up the center a short distance from the tip. Metal pen points that fit into a wooden handle came into use only about a hundred years ago. They are shaped like the reed and quill pen points.

When you dip any of these pens into ink, a little ink clings to the hollowed-out undersurface of the point. Then, as you write, ink flows from the storage space, or *reservoir,* through the narrow slit, to the tip and onto the paper.

The ink does not flow to the tip under its own weight. If it did, most of the ink would flow from the tip as soon as you lifted the pen from the bottle. The ink is fed from the reservoir to the tip of the pen by *capillary action.*

You can see an example of capillary action by looking at a glass of water. You will see that the water that touches the glass sides climbs a little way up the glass.

You can see another example of capillary action by dipping the end of a piece of cloth or blotting paper into water. The water climbs up the tiny fibers of cloth or paper. A candle wick and the wicks of old-fashioned oil lamps also work by capillary action.

The old-fashioned straight pens that we have described don't hold much ink, so they have to be dipped frequently. Fountain pens, however, have a larger reservoir for storing ink. The reservoir may be a rubber bulb, or it may be simply a "tank" inside the pen handle.

To fill the pen, depending on what type you have, you pull a little lever, or turn or pull out the top end of the pen. This pushes the air and any remaining ink out of the reservoir.

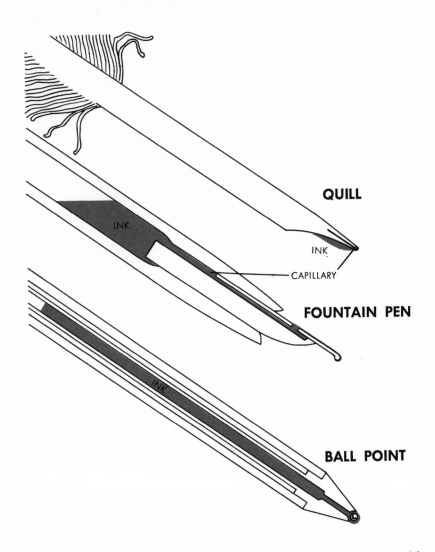

QUILL

INK

INK

CAPILLARY

FOUNTAIN PEN

INK

BALL POINT

When you move the lever or top back to its original position, the reservoir is left almost empty—but not for long. The weight of the atmosphere pressing down on the surface of the ink in the bottle pushes ink into the pen and fills the reservoir within a few seconds. Some fountain pens have removable ink tanks, or cartridges, that can be replaced.

Ball point pens work in a different way. The ink is contained in a thin metal or plastic tube that is sealed at the top and holds a tiny round ball at the point. The ink has to be just the right thickness so that it will flow down onto the ball, but will not run out. Because the surface of the ball is not perfectly smooth, the ball picks up ink inside the tube and transfers it to the paper as you make the ball roll along when you write.

Much of the world depends on electricity to light buildings and streets, to run appliances, to aid communications, and to serve many other purposes. But have you ever realized that it is just as important to turn off electric power as it is to turn it on? So, there are hundreds of kinds of switches on the market. There are manual switches and automatic switches, snap-action switches and mercury switches, two-way switches and three-way switches.

ELECTRIC SWITCH

Do you know how a flick of a switch turns on a light? A switch joins or "breaks" two wires that carry an electric current (*see diagrams*).

When you push the plug of a lamp cord into a wall outlet, the prongs of the plug connect with wires that carry electricity from an electric power plant to your house and back again. If the switch in the lamp is "closed," the wires are joined and the current

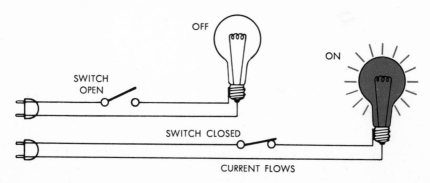

OFF

ON

SWITCH
OPEN

SWITCH CLOSED

CURRENT FLOWS

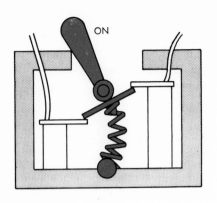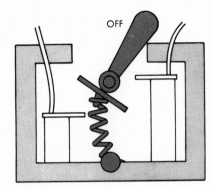

SNAP-ACTION SWITCH

flows through one of the wires, lights up the bulb as it passes through, and returns through the other wire back to the power plant. This is called a closed *circuit*. When the switch is "open," there is a break in one wire. This break prevents electricity from flowing through the circuit to light up the bulb. When this happens, we say the circuit is open.

Switches You Often Use

One common electric switch found in homes is the "snap-action" switch. If you snap the toggle "on," a spring clicks the switch to the closed position and the light goes on. What happens is that a metal collar on the toggle joins the two wires so the current can

MERCURY SWITCH

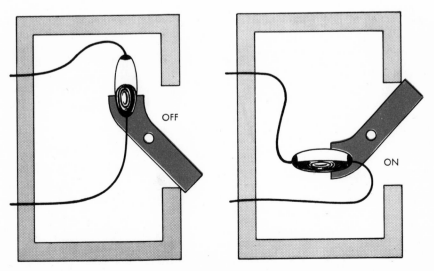

complete the circuit. When you turn the toggle "off," you lift the collar and break the circuit.

Have you ever worked a "silent" switch, or mercury switch? Mercury is a metal that stays liquid at room temperatures. In a mercury switch, a small capsule with mercury inside is attached to the end of the toggle. The wires that carry the current run into the ends of the capsule. When you flick the toggle to "on," the capsule moves from an upright to a level position. The mercury spreads the length of the capsule, connects the two wires, and current flows through the mercury. When the toggle is turned "off," the capsule is tilted up. Then the mercury runs to the bottom of the capsule. This breaks the circuit and the current cannot flow from one wire to another.

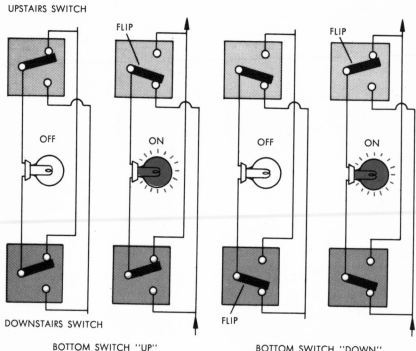

UPSTAIRS SWITCH

FLIP

OFF   ON   OFF   ON

DOWNSTAIRS SWITCH   FLIP

BOTTOM SWITCH "UP"   BOTTOM SWITCH "DOWN"

How can a stairway light be turned on or off from either of two switches—one at the bottom of the stairs, the other at the top? Each of the two switches is connected to the light and also to the wires that bring electricity into the house and back to the power station (*see diagram*). The circuit can be opened or closed by flipping either switch, no matter which position the other switch is in.

Although circuit breakers are becoming in-creasingly popular in electrical systems today, there are still quite a few places where fuses can be found—in homes, in machines, in auto-mobiles, and even in strings of Christmas tree lights. Fuses are said to be our most misun-derstood protective devices. They are used to prevent fires, but many people do not appreciate this fact, and try to eliminate fuses by wiring around them or putting a penny behind them.

ELECTRIC FUSE

A fuse is a kind of switch that automatically opens an electrical circuit when the fuse gets hot enough to melt. It is usually a short piece of lead (or lead with other metals added to it) that melts at a lower temperature than the rest of the metal wire in the circuit. (Some homes are equipped with circuit breakers that work by magnetic attraction.)

When more current flows through a circuit than the wires are designed to carry, they may heat up enough to set fire to wood or other nearby material. They heat up when the insulation wears off a lamp cord, allowing the two wires within the cord to touch. Or they heat up if a circuit is "overloaded." For example, when too many lamps and other appliances are being used at the same time, all the lights in the circuit may suddenly go out. A fuse has melted, opening the circuit and stopping the flow of electric current before the wires got dangerously hot.

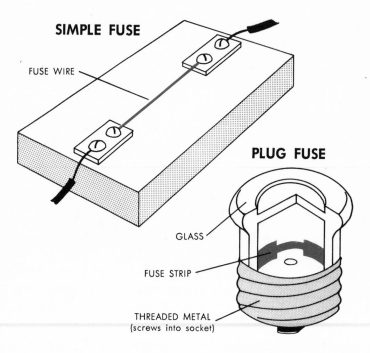

SIMPLE FUSE

FUSE WIRE

PLUG FUSE

GLASS

FUSE STRIP

THREADED METAL
(screws into socket)

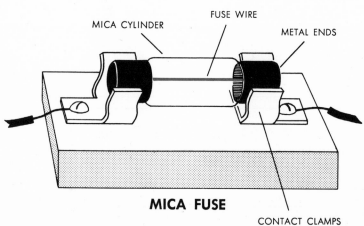

MICA CYLINDER

FUSE WIRE

METAL ENDS

MICA FUSE

CONTACT CLAMPS

In the case of the combination lock, there is no danger of forgetting your key, since you don't need one. The only danger is in losing your memory. Since more people lose keys than develop amnesia, the combination lock has become very popular on schoolhouse lockers, bank vaults, and bicycle chains. A normal, average type of combination lock may have from one hundred thousand to one million possible combinations, but only one of them will open the lock.

COMBINATION LOCK

A combination padlock is handy for locking your school locker or bicycle, because it opens without a key. To open it, all you have to know is the "combination"—usually a series of three numbers—and which way to turn the dial to line up the first number of the combination with a notch on the face of the lock. Here is how it works.

Inside the lock there are three small wheels. One of the wheels, called the *drive wheel,* is attached to the *shaft* so that it turns with the dial (*see Diagram 1*). The other two wheels turn freely around the *spindle*. One end of the spindle fits into the end of the shaft, the other end is attached to the lock case. (The shaft and spindle may be arranged differently in some kinds of locks.)

Each wheel has a slot cut into its edge. Each outer wheel has a small metal *post* sticking out from the side toward the center wheel.

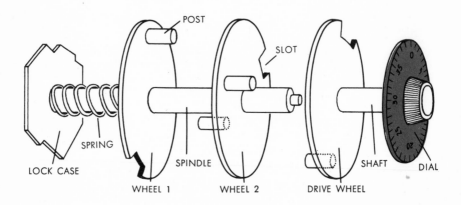

The center wheel has a post on each side. Each of the two "free" wheels will turn only when the post on its side is pushed by the post on the wheel next to it.

To open the lock, you first turn the dial all the way around twice in the same direction, say to the right. This brings the posts of all three wheels together so that they all turn with the dial. When you stop turning the dial at the first number of the combination, the wheel farthest from the dial is set with the slot in its edge at a certain point (*see Diagram 2A*).

Next, you turn the dial one full turn in the opposite direction (left), then on to the second number of the combination. This leaves the first wheel unmoved and turns the middle wheel so that its slot is lined up with the slot in the first wheel (*see Diagram 2B*). Finally, you turn the dial again in the opposite direction (right) to the third number of the combination. This turns only the drive wheel and brings its slot into line with the slots in the other two wheels (*see Diagram 2C*).

Now a tug on the lock pulls the *shackle*—the curved bar that fits through the holes on your locker and its door—part way out of the lock. As the shackle moves, a *hook* near one end pulls the *locking lever* upward (*see Diagram 3*). The locking lever rocks on a pin through its middle, pushing the other end of the lever into the

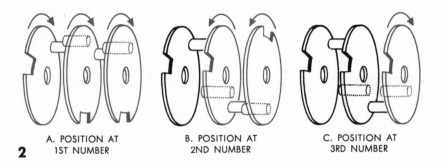

A. POSITION AT
1ST NUMBER

B. POSITION AT
2ND NUMBER

C. POSITION AT
3RD NUMBER

2

slots in the edges of the wheels. This releases the hook so that the end of the shackle can come out of the lock.

When you push the shackle back into the lock, the hook presses the end of the locking lever downward, lifting the other end of the lever out of the wheel slots. A spin of the dial turns the wheels so that the lock can't be opened until the wheel slots are brought back into line.

A lock like this one, with 40 marks on its dial, could have 64,000 possible combinations. Can you figure out what you would have to change to make it open with a different combination?

3

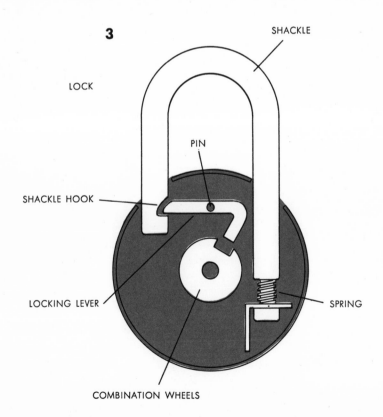

SHACKLE

LOCK

PIN

SHACKLE HOOK

LOCKING LEVER

SPRING

COMBINATION WHEELS

Since the dawn of recorded history, man has looked for ways to protect his property and himself. The story of locks is an old one— hundreds of years old. Actually, most locks are just highly refined applications of the old-fashioned bolt on the door. Be it padlock, door lock, ignition lock, or any other kind of lock, if it opens with a key, it usually works like this.

DOOR LOCK

Your door key probably is a flat piece of metal with grooves and ridges along the sides, and peaks and valleys along the top. The grooves and ridges match and slide along grooves and ridges

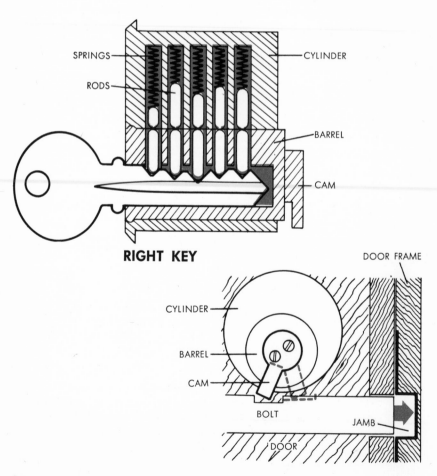

in the keyhole. If they didn't match, the key would not fit into the lock.

The peaks and valleys along the top make your key different from the key to any other lock. They are designed to match a row of little rods—each different in length from the others. The rods are held in channels that run between the lock *cylinder* and the lock *barrel*. There are two small rods in each channel. A spring pushes down from the top of the channel and holds the ends of the two rods together (*see diagram*).

As you push the key into the lock, the rods ride up and down along the peaks and valleys until the key is all the way in. At this point the tops of the lower rods are lined up with the top of the barrel. The barrel is the part of the lock that you turn to open the door. Since the rod ends all line up, the barrel can be turned.

Attached to the end of the barrel is a lever, or *cam*. The cam extends down into a slot cut in the *bolt*. It is the bolt, which slides back and forth, that prevents you from opening the door.

When you turn the barrel one way with your key, the cam turns and pushes the bolt into the *jamb*, or hole in the door frame. When you turn the key in the other direction, this pulls the bolt out of the jamb and unlocks the door so it can be opened.

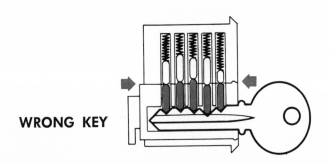

WRONG KEY

What happens when the wrong key is used? It may slide into the keyhole all right, because the grooves and ridges along the side of two keys may be the same. But as the key slides in, the tops of the lower rods will not line up. If only one rod is out of line with the edge of the barrel, then the barrel cannot be turned.

Locksmiths carry a whole stock of different size rods. They can change your lock in a few minutes by changing the rods or by rearranging them in a different order in the barrel. A new key is then required.

The fireplace used to be an essential part of every well-built home. The cooking was done on it, people read by the light of the blaze, they told stories in front of it, and, of course, the fire warmed them during the winter. Today a fireplace is a luxury, but it is still good to gather in front of the burning embers or even an artificial log connected to a gas jet.

FIREPLACE

A fireplace is more than just a cave in the wall to burn logs in and a pipe to carry out the smoke. To keep the fire supplied with air, so that it burns steadily, and to keep the smoke moving up through the chimney instead of into the room, a fireplace must be shaped in a certain way and adjusted properly.

A well-designed fireplace has a back that slopes forward as it rises to a long, narrow opening that leads to the *flue,* or passage up through the chimney (*see diagram*). The long, narrow opening is called the *throat.* It can be opened or closed by adjusting a hinged metal door called the *damper.* (When the fireplace is not in use, the damper is usually left closed, to keep cold air and dirt from coming down the chimney into the room. The damper should be opened before the fire is lighted.)

The fireplace works because when air is heated, it expands and becomes lighter than the colder air around it. The fire heats the air around it in the fireplace, and this heated air—with smoke mixed in—is pushed up by cooler air through the throat and flue and out the top of the chimney. The cool air from the room flows into the fireplace and supplies oxygen to keep the fire burning.

By adjusting the damper to change the size of the throat opening, you can control the amount of air flowing into the fireplace and out the flue. In this way, you can keep the fire burning steadily, but not too fast.

Behind the damper is a trough, called the smoke box (*see diagram*). When cool air sometimes pours down the chimney, it collects in the smoke box, where it is warmed up and moves back up the flue. The smoke box also provides a place for smoke to collect when a draft of air blows down the chimney and stops the usual flue action.

A tall chimney helps protect the fire against being disturbed by winds that swirl around the roof. Experts recommend a height

FLUE

SMOKE BOX

DAMPER
(partly open)

THROAT

of at least 35 feet from the fireplace grate to the chimney top, and the top should be at least two feet above the peak of the roof. The flue should be round or square rather than rectangular to ease the flow of air, and a cross section of the flue should have an area of at least 60 square inches.

If a house is tightly sealed, with weather stripping around all the doors and windows, the fireplace may have trouble drawing in more air, and the fire will die down. The answer is to open a window, preferably upstairs, so the incoming air will be warmed before it flows around your guests seated around the fireplace.

There are several kinds of fire extinguishers and they will put out different kinds of fires. It is essential that we know what kinds of extinguishers will put out what kinds of fires. In the United States alone, fires destroy more than one billion dollars worth of property and kill over six thousand people annually.

FIRE EXTINGUISHER

One of the most common types of fire-fighting equipment is the *soda-acid extinguisher,* which uses water to put out a fire. Here is a way to find out how it works. Mix as much bicarbonate of soda as you can in a glass of lukewarm water. As you keep adding more and more of the white powder, there will come a time when no more will dissolve. When this happens, pour in one or two teaspoonfuls of vinegar (which is a weak acid). What happens? The gas that forms is carbon dioxide.

The tank of a soda-acid extinguisher is nearly full of water containing bicarbonate of soda. At the top of the tank is a small bottle of sulfuric acid. When the extinguisher is turned upside down, the acid mixes with the soda in the water and forms carbon dioxide gas. As this gas expands, or spreads out, it forces the water out through a hose to wet the fire.

A *pressurized water extinguisher* contains water and compressed air. When you squeeze the handles, a valve opens and the compressed air forces the water out. These water extinguishers work best on small fires of paper, cloth, wood, and trash.

A *foam extinguisher* works like a soda-acid extinguisher, but along with water, it sprays liquid foam that looks something like shaving cream from a spray can. This foam covers the burning surface and keeps air from reaching it. Without getting oxygen from the air, a fire cannot burn.

A *carbon dioxide extinguisher* uses the gas itself to smother the fire. Carbon dioxide gas is stored under pressure inside this extinguisher. When you press the handles together, a valve opens and sprays the gas through a horn-shaped tube onto the fire.

SODA-ACID WATER EXTINGUISHER

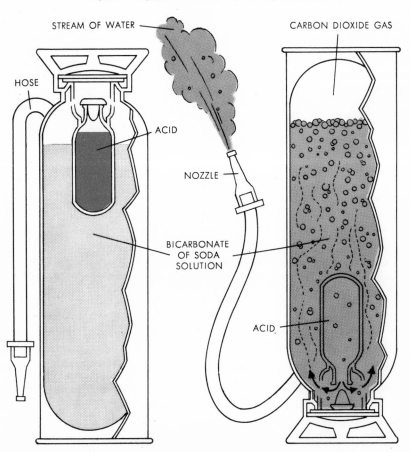

STREAM OF WATER

CARBON DIOXIDE GAS

HOSE

ACID

NOZZLE

BICARBONATE OF SODA SOLUTION

ACID

A new kind of fire extinguisher can be used on nearly all kinds of fires. It is called a *dry-chemical extinguisher*. Air under pressure inside the extinguisher forces a fine powder through the hose onto the fire. The powder is mostly bicarbonate of soda, which smothers the fire.

There are three main classes of fires (*see table*). Can you guess why water-filled extinguishers should not be used on burning liquids? Why wouldn't carbon-dioxide extinguishers be used on large Class A fires?

Fire extinguishers should be used only in emergencies. If the chemicals are released, an extinguisher will be useless in case of fire, and the chemicals may injure someone.

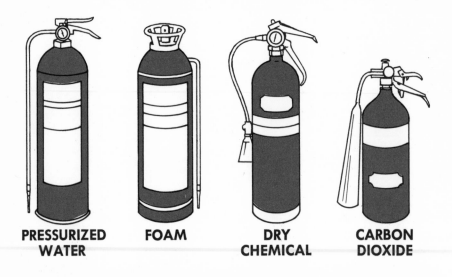

PRESSURIZED WATER   **FOAM**   **DRY CHEMICAL**   **CARBON DIOXIDE**

TYPE OF EXTINGUISHER TO USE

TYPE OF FIRE	WATER (Soda-acid or pressurized)	FOAM	CARBON DIOXIDE	DRY CHEMICAL
CLASS A FIRE (wood, paper, cloth, trash)	YES	YES	YES (if fire is small)	YES (if fire is small)
CLASS B FIRE (burning liquids— gasoline, oil, paint, cooking fat)	NO	YES	YES	YES
CLASS C FIRE (electrical equipment— motors, appliances, switches)	NO	NO	YES	YES

The toilet works as a siphon to remove waste materials from the bowl through a drain pipe and into a sewer or a septic tank. Considering the many valves, shut-off points, rubber washers, and other types of seals necessary to keep this device working properly, it is amazing how few times it needs to be repaired. And when something does go wrong, it can usually be fixed by a simple replacement of parts.

TOILET

The bowl of a toilet is shaped something like a large funnel with a "spout" that is bent upward in a U-shape. The spout is hidden behind the back of the bowl, and it is connected to the drain pipe (*see Diagram 1A*). Most of the time the bowl and spout are partly filled with water. (The water in the spout seals it off so that no unpleasant odors can come into your bathroom through the drain pipe.)

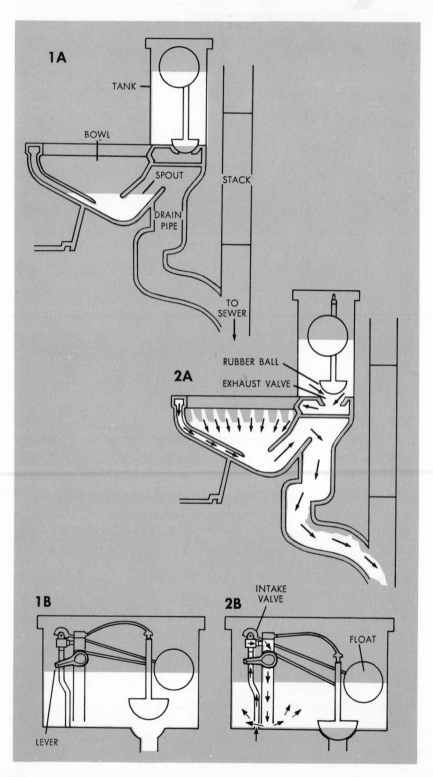

1A

TANK

BOWL

SPOUT

DRAIN PIPE

STACK

TO SEWER

RUBBER BALL

EXHAUST VALVE

2A

1B

2B

INTAKE VALVE

FLOAT

LEVER

When you flush the toilet, from four to six gallons of water flow from the tank through the rim of the bowl and down into the bowl. This water piles up in the bowl and pushes some of the water in the spout over the edge of the spout into the drain pipe (*see Diagram 1B*). The spout and drain pipe form a siphon, and water flowing through it carries off waste materials from the bowl into the drain pipe. The siphon action continues until the bowl is empty. Then some of the clear water that is left in the spout flows back into the bowl.

In most toilet systems, the main drain pipe, or *stack*, sticks up through the roof of the building and is open. Unpleasant odors escape through it, and the air pressing in from the stack stops the siphon action when the bowl is empty, so that some water is left in the spout.

How the Tank Refills

After the toilet is flushed, water flows into the tank until it reaches the proper level. If you lift the top off of the tank you can see how this works and what keeps the water from overflowing.

Push the lever to flush the toilet. The other end of the lever lifts a rod that pulls a rubber ball (or something similar) out of the hole in the bottom of the tank (*see Diagram 2A*). Opening this *exhaust valve* lets water flow to the bowl. As the level of the water drops in the tank, a hollow ball, called the *float* moves down with the water. The float is connected to the *intake valve* by a rod that works like the handle on a faucet. When the tank is nearly empty, the rubber ball drops into the hole, closing the exhaust valve. And when the float nears the bottom of the tank, its rod opens the intake valve, letting water flow into the tank from a water pipe (*see Diagram 2B*).

Sometimes the rubber ball fails to drop into the hole. When this happens, water flowing into the tank keeps running into the bowl. You can stop this waste of water by pushing the ball down into the exhaust hole.

As the tank fills up, the float rises, lifting the rod until the water reaches the proper level in the tank and the intake valve is closed. In this way, the amount of water left in the tank controls the intake of water into the tank. This is called *control by feedback,* because the float "feeds back" information about the level of the water in the tank to the intake valve. Control by feedback is used in many kinds of machines, chemical processes, and electronic devices. A thermostat works by feedback. So does an automatic tire pump.

Ancient Rome was probably the first large city to transport water to central places where it could be drawn without taking a long walk to a river, lake, or stream. The Romans built aqueducts, some of which were fifty miles long. We use pipes today, but our system of water distribution is very similar to the one used in Rome so long ago. However, many parts of the world are faced with a water shortage these days, and so the key to water conservation may be the properly operating water faucet.

FAUCET

Have you ever wondered how a faucet works, or why a faucet sometimes drips even though it is turned off?

The parts of a faucet we usually see are the handle and the spout where the water comes out. As the diagram shows, the faucet handle is at the end of a metal rod. On the other end of the rod is a washer. It is a ring of rubber, fiber, or plastic with a hole in the middle. A screw fits through this hole and holds the washer to the rod.

When you turn the faucet handle to the left, the metal rod moves and the washer is moved away from the opening of the water pipe.

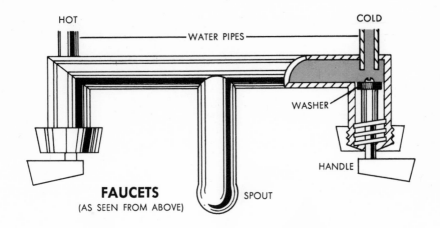

HOT   WATER PIPES   COLD

WASHER

HANDLE

FAUCETS   SPOUT
(AS SEEN FROM ABOVE)

Water then flows out of the spout. When you turn the faucet handle to the right, the washer plugs the opening of the water pipe and the water flow is stopped.

One cause of a dripping faucet is a worn-out washer. To fix a leaky faucet, first turn off the water supply by turning the valve handle on the pipe below the sink. Then replace the old faucet washer with a new one. The valves on water pipes rarely leak, because they have a metal washer that fits tightly into the opening that water flows through (*see valve diagram*). Even though this type of washer does not leak, it is not used in faucets. The reason is that it takes too much effort to close the valve tightly and to open it.

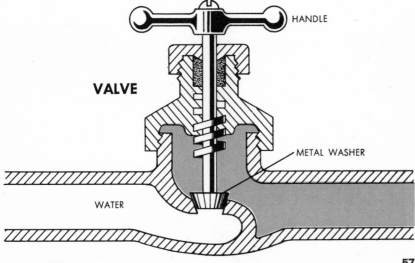

HANDLE

VALVE

METAL WASHER

WATER

MEASUREMENT

Almost seven thousand years ago, the ancient Egyptians were using scales to measure the weight of grain. They used a balance scale. It wasn't until 1831 that Thaddeus Fairbanks patented the first platform scale. But since that time, business in the scale factories has been booming. If there is a weight watcher in every house, as there seems to be, there is also a bathroom scale to tell him how he is doing.

SCALE

A scale measures the weight of something by comparing it to things whose weight we already know. One way to do this is with a *balance scale*. This is a small seesaw with a pan hanging from each end (*see diagram*).

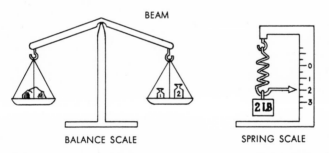

BEAM

BALANCE SCALE   SPRING SCALE

When the thing to be weighed—say a stone—is placed in one pan, it pulls the *beam* down on that side and up on the other side. Things whose weight you know can then be placed in the other pan until the two pans are brought to the same level. Adding the weights of these things gives you the weight of the stone. (Chemists and druggists often use balance scales, because they measure weight so accurately. But imagine how hard it would be to weigh yourself on a balance scale!)

Another way to weigh something is to hang it from a spring. The heavier the weight the more the spring will stretch. First you *calibrate* the scale by hanging objects of different weight—say 1 pound, 2 pounds, and so on—from the spring and marking how far the end of the spring is stretched by each weight (*see diagram*). If you hung a large stone from the spring and found that it pulled the end of the spring to a point halfway between 1 and 2 on the scale, you would know the stone weighed 1½ pounds.

Hanging from a Spring in Your Bathroom

You may be surprised to find out that when you stand on the *platform* of a bathroom scale, you are hanging from a spring (*see Diagram 1*). Your weight pushes down the platform, which in turn pushes down on two triangle-shaped plates. These plates are *levers,* supported on *fulcrums,* or posts, at two corners. The unsupported corner of each of these levers pushes down on a third triangular lever whose moving corner is hooked to the end of the spring. These levers bring weight from all parts of the platform to bear on the spring, so it doesn't matter where you stand on the platform.

As the spring stretches, a V-shaped piece of metal attached to the end of the spring turns and pulls the *rack* toward the spring (*see Diagram 2*). The rack has teeth something like those on a saw blade. When the rack moves, it turns a long, thin gear, called a *pinion,* at the other end of the scale. A pointer attached to the pinion turns with it, showing how much the spring has stretched, and pointing to your weight on the scale's dial.

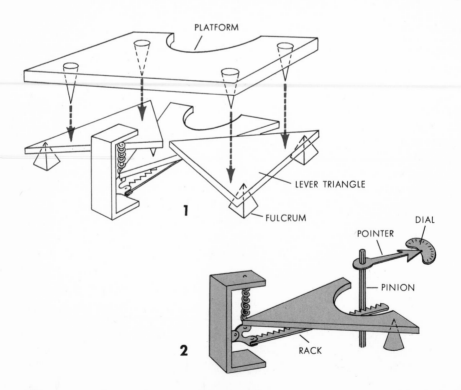

PLATFORM

LEVER TRIANGLE

1

FULCRUM

DIAL

POINTER

PINION

2

RACK

Some of the most popular television per-sonalities are the weathermen and weathergirls. It seems that man always wants to know how hot he is or how cold he is, more precisely he wants to know how hot or cold the air around him is. He also measures the temperature of his cooking, his swimming hole, and his automo-bile engine. The thermometer has been around for a long time. Galileo developed one in 1593, and Fahrenheit built his first mercury thermom-eter in 1714.

THERMOMETER

You can get some idea of how warm or cold the air is from the way it feels on your skin. But to measure just how warm or cold anything is, or find its *temperature,* you must use a thermometer. Although there are many different kinds of thermometers, those most commonly used all work the same way.

The household thermometer is simply a sealed glass tube with a small glass bulb at one end. The bulb is filled with alcohol (usually colored red so you can see it easily) or mercury, a silvery-colored liquid metal. Mercury gives the more exact reading, and is used in most laboratory and medical thermometers. But alcohol freezes at a much lower temperature than mercury, and is therefore used in most outdoor thermometers.

When the air warms up, it heats the alcohol or mercury and makes it *expand,* or swell. The only space the liquid can expand into is the

METAL THERMOMETER

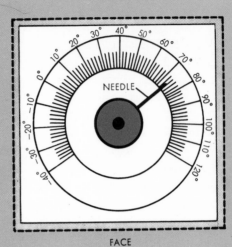

NEEDLE

FACE

LIQUID THERMOMETER

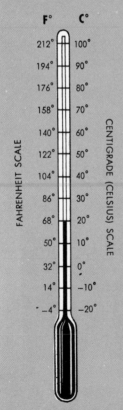

F°	C°
212°	100°
194°	90°
176°	80°
158°	70°
140°	60°
122°	50°
104°	40°
86°	30°
68°	20°
50°	10°
32°	0°
14°	-10°
-4°	-20°

FAHRENHEIT SCALE

CENTIGRADE (CELSIUS) SCALE

SPRING

BACK

channel in the tube, so it rises in the tube as it gets warmer. When the air grows cooler, the liquid loses its heat to the air and *contracts,* or shrinks, dropping down toward the bulb.

Two Ways to Measure Temperature

The rise and fall of the liquid tell you only that the air is getting warmer or cooler. To measure how much the temperature is changing, or just how warm or cold the air is, you need a scale of measurement. This scale is usually printed on the board to which the thermometer is attached, or it may be marked on the glass tube.

The household thermometer scale measures temperature in *degrees Fahrenheit.* This scale was devised early in the 1700s by German physicist Gabriel Fahrenheit. There are different stories of how he decided on this scale. One is that he set a thermometer in a mixture of ice and salt and marked the lowest point to which the mercury dropped, 0° (zero degrees). He marked 100° at the level of mercury when it was as warm as the human body (we know now that normal human temperature is 98.6° F.). Then he divided the space between these points into 100 equal degrees. Water freezes at 32° F. and boils at 212° F.

Temperature is usually measured by the Fahrenheit scale in English-speaking countries, Germany, and the Scandinavian countries. But people in all other countries and scientists everywhere use a simpler scale, called the *Centigrade* or *Celsius* scale (for Swedish astronomer Anders Celsius, who first suggested it in 1742). On this scale, water freezes at 0° C. and boils at 100° C.

You can easily change a temperature reading from Centigrade to Fahrenheit. Multiply the Centigrade reading by 9, divide by 5, and add 32°. To change a Fahrenheit temperature reading to Centigrade, subtract 32° from the Fahrenheit reading, multiply by 5, then divide by 9.

Since everything expands when it is heated, several other kinds of thermometers are based on this rule. For example, scientists sometimes use a thermometer that has a sealed container filled with gas. As the gas gets warmer, it can't expand, so it presses harder on the container. Measuring this increase in pressure gives the change in temperature.

Metal thermometers are also fairly common. They look something like a small clock. Inside is a coiled metal spring, something like a watch spring, with one end attached to a needle on the face of the thermometer. As heat expands the coiled spring, it unwinds slightly, turning the needle on the dial so it points to the correct temperature.

The barometer is one of the most essential tools of the weatherman as well as being a boon to the sailor. There are two kinds of barometers. One of them, the mercury barometer, was invented by an Italian scientist, Evangelista Torricelli, in 1643. There is also the aneroid barometer, but scientists still use the mercury barometer because it is the most accurate instrument for measuring air pressure.

BAROMETER

To forecast the weather, weathermen must know how much the air above a particular place weighs, how warm or cold the air is, and how much water vapor it contains.

These men measure the weight of the air, or air pressure, with a *barometer*. The pressure of the atmosphere over your city, or any other place, changes from hour to hour or from day to day as the air around you becomes warmer or cooler. Because cool air is heavier than warm air, cool air presses harder against a barometer than warm air.

The mercury barometer is a narrow glass tube a little more than 30 inches long, closed at one end. It is filled with mercury and then placed open end down in an open basin, or *reservoir,* of mercury. The mercury in the tube drops down a few inches, leaving a *vacuum,* or space with almost no air in it, at the closed end.

What keeps the mercury standing in the tube? The air presses down on the surface of the mercury in the reservoir and holds up the mercury in the tube. When the air gets heavier, it pushes the mercury higher in the tube. When the air gets lighter, it presses less on the mercury in the reservoir, so the mercury in the tube drops lower.

A scale near the top of the tube shows exactly how many inches the top of the column of mercury is above the surface of the mercury in the reservoir. Weather reports usually give the barometer readings in inches and tell whether the air pressure is rising or falling.

Air pressure can also be measured with an *aneroid barometer,* which looks something like a dial thermometer or a clock. You may have seen an aneroid barometer hanging on a wall or sitting on a desk.

Inside the aneroid barometer is a small, disk-shaped metal can from which most of the air has been removed. As the air pressure out-

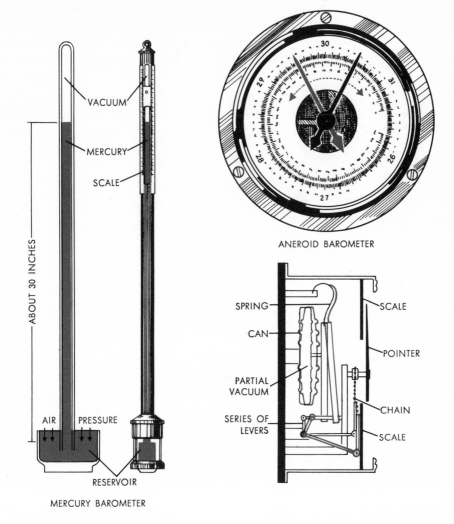

VACUUM

MERCURY

SCALE

ABOUT 30 INCHES

AIR | PRESSURE

RESERVOIR

MERCURY BAROMETER

ANEROID BAROMETER

SPRING

CAN

PARTIAL VACUUM

SERIES OF LEVERS

SCALE

POINTER

CHAIN

SCALE

side of the can increases, it pushes the surface of the metal can inward. As the air pressure outside the can decreases, the air in the can pushes the surface of the can outward.

The motion of the can surface is too small to see. However, the movement is made larger when it is carried by a series of levers and a chain to a pointer on the barometer scale. The pointer moves with the changes of air pressure and the scale is arranged so that it shows the same readings (in inches) as a mercury barometer.

Air pressure also decreases as you get higher above the level of the sea. Barometers in different places have to be adjusted so that the difference in pressure due to difference in altitude is not measured along with the changes in air pressure.

The mercury barometer can be adjusted by simply moving the scale up or down. An aneroid barometer is adjusted by turning a knob that tightens or loosens a spring attached to the can surface.

Man is a fanatic about time. He wants to measure everything, from a mile relay run to the speed of light. Water clocks were used three thousand years ago. Sundials are even older. The first clock having wheels, a dial, and an hour hand was invented in the 1300s. Over the centuries, clockmakers added a pendulum, a minute hand, and a second hand. Not much new was added until the electric motor was attached to it. Here's what makes it tick.

CLOCK

A clock measures time by moving its hands around the dial so that they always turn the same distance in the same period of time. It has to have a *driving mechanism* to turn the hands and a *regulator* to keep them moving at the same speed.

Most of our clocks and watches are driven by a spring something like the coiled strip of metal that turns the wheels of a toy wind-up automobile. The *mainspring* of a clock is coiled inside a metal drum. One end of the spring is attached to the side of the drum, and the other end is attached to the winding shaft at the center of the drum (*see diagram*).

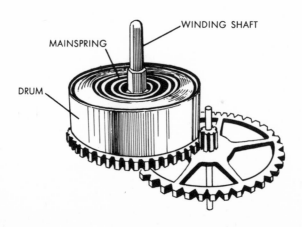

When you wind a clock, you turn the inside end of the spring around and around, bending it into a tighter coil. As the spring unbends, it pushes the drum around the shaft. The drum has gear teeth around its edges, and as the drum goes around, it turns a series of gears that make the hands of the clock go around.

If there were nothing to slow down the turning of these gears, the mainspring would unwind in a few moments, like the spring of a wind-up toy. But one of the gears turns a wheel with long, slanted teeth sticking out from the edge. This is called the *escape wheel.* Next to the escape wheel is a bar, called the *pallet,* that rocks back and forth on an axle at the center of the bar. At each end of the pallet there is a hook (*see diagram below*). When one end of the pallet rocks toward the escape wheel, the hook on that end blocks

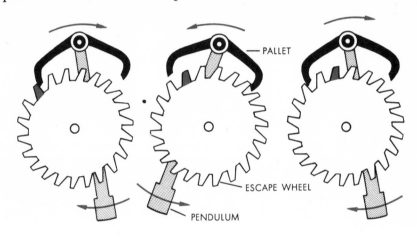

a tooth on the escape wheel and stops it from turning. When the pallet rocks the other way, that tooth is no longer blocked. The escape wheel turns just a little way before the other hook blocks a tooth on the escape wheel. Each tick you hear is the sound of an escape wheel tooth striking a hook. But what makes the pallet rock back and forth?

Some clocks have a *pendulum* attached to the center of the pallet bar. A pendulum is a weight that hangs from the end of a string or rod and swings back and forth. If you have ever experimented with a pendulum, you know that it swings back and forth faster as you shorten the string or rod. The pendulum of a clock is just long enough so that it swings back and forth in one second, or 60 times a minute. This rocks the pallet bar back and forth once each second and keeps the escape wheel—and the other gears in the clock—turning at just the right speed.

You may wonder what keeps the pendulum swinging back and

forth. The end of each pallet is slanted so that as the pallet lifts out of the way of a tooth in the escape wheel, the tooth gives it a slight push.

Circular Pendulums

Watches and many clocks are regulated by a circular pendulum called a *balance wheel* (*see diagram*). The balance wheel is heavier around the edges than in the center. It is turned by a forked rod attached to the pallet. When the pallet rocks one way, the balance wheel turns part way around on its axle. As the balance wheel turns, it winds up a tiny coil spring, called the *hairspring*. The spring winds up until it is tight enough to push the balance wheel back in the opposite direction. This rocks the pallet the other way and frees the escape wheel for one more short turn.

The speed of the escape wheel regulates the speed of all the other gears in the clock. But how do these three hands turn at different speeds if they are all attached at the center of the clock? The answer is that each hand is fastened to a different shaft, one inside the other. The two outside shafts, of course, are hollow.

Many clocks today are driven by electric motors. An electric clock has no escape wheel. The speed of the clock's moving parts is regulated by the *frequency* of the electric current fed into the motor. The frequency is the number of times each second that the current reverses its direction. In the United States, alternating current changes its direction 60 times each second. Since there are 60 seconds in a minute and 60 minutes in an hour, it is easy to arrange gears to turn the clock hands at the right speeds.

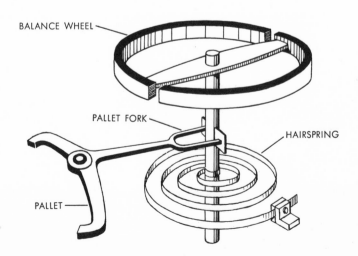

BALANCE WHEEL

PALLET FORK

HAIRSPRING

PALLET

How much do you owe the power company for the electricity you have used? The obvious answer is to calculate the bill based upon how much electrical energy has gone into the house over a certain period of time. That is what the electric meter does. It was invented by Oliver B. Shallenberger, who built the first practical model in 1888—only nine years after Edison developed his first incandescent light bulb.

ELECTRIC METER

Whenever a light or other electrical device is switched on in your house, a glass-enclosed meter in your basement or on the outside of the house is recording how much electric current is being used. Every month or two, a man comes to "read" the meter, so that the power company can figure out how much electricity you have used and send you a bill. Here is how the meter works.

The electric current from the power company's wires flows through the meter on its way to and from the wires in your house. Inside the meter, the current passes through the coils of a small electric motor—something like the motor in an electric clock. The coils are made of wire wound around iron cores, and they are arranged so that the edge of a thin disk of aluminum can turn between the coils (*see diagram*).

The current does not flow steadily in one direction through the coils, but *alternates*, or changes its direction, 60 times each second. Each time the current changes direction in the wire, the coils become *electromagnets* and give a magnetic "pull" that turns the aluminum disk. The more lights and other electrical appliances you are using, the more current is flowing through the coils. This makes the magnetic "pulls" stronger than before, so the disk turns faster.

The shaft of the turning disk is connected by gears and other shafts to the pointers on the *register* dials (*see diagram*). Each dial is numbered from 0 to 9, and the gears are arranged so that one complete turn of the pointer on one dial—from 0 around to 0—

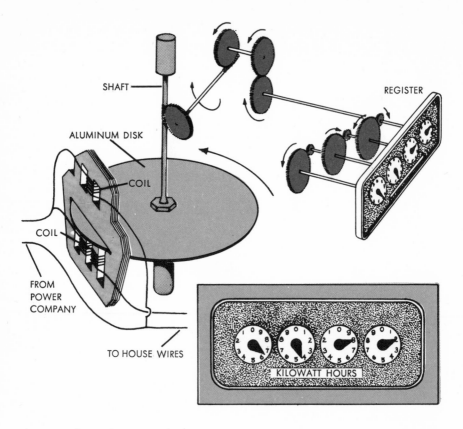

SHAFT

REGISTER

ALUMINUM DISK

COIL

COIL

FROM
POWER
COMPANY

TO HOUSE WIRES

KILOWATT HOURS

moves the pointer on the next dial to the left just one number, say from 0 to 1. (Notice that each dial is numbered in the opposite direction from the dial beside it.)

How Much Electric Power Do You Use?

Electric power is measured in *watts,* a unit named for James Watt, the Scotsman who invented the steam engine. A 100-watt light bulb draws 100 watts of electric power as long as it is switched on. If it is lighted for one hour, it uses 100 *watt-hours* of electric power. Because so much electric power is used today, the electric meter measures the power you use in *kilowatt-hours,* or 1,000 watt-hours.

To read the number of kilowatt hours your meter has recorded, read the dials from left to right—the number on each dial that the pointer has *just passed.* (The meter in the diagram reads 6,482 kilowatt-hours.) At the end of a month, read the meter again. Subtract the first reading from the second, and you will have the number of kilowatt-hours of electric power you and your family have used in that month.

Although radar was given a great deal of credit for speeding the Allied victory toward the end of World War II, its history goes back to 1922. It was developed by two men named Taylor and Young of the United States Naval Research Aircraft Laboratory, and the Navy put a radar installation on the U.S.S. New York in 1938. In the meantime, the British developed their own radar, which they called radiolocation. Today, many pleasure boats and fishing boats as well as warships are equipped with this device.

RADAR

If you have ever heard an echo, you already know something about radar. You can sometimes hear the sound of your voice bouncing back from a hill, a cliff, a building, or the far end of a cave. You may also have seen a giant searchlight sending a beam of light into the sky. When the searchlight's beam strikes a cloud, you see the cloud because light is reflected from it back to your eyes.

You can use echoes to figure out the distance to a cliff by the length of time it takes sound to travel to the cliff and return. Sound travels through the air about 1,100 feet each second. Suppose it took one second (half a second to the cliff and another half second back) to hear your echo after you shouted. In half a second the sound would have traveled 550 feet, which would be the distance to the cliff.

In much the same way, we can use radar waves to find the distance to objects. But instead of sound waves, radar uses radio waves. Radio waves travel at the speed of light—186,000 miles each second. Radar takes its name from "RAdio Detection And Ranging."

Radar waves are sent out in *pulses,* or short bursts, with pauses between pulses. Each pulse from the transmitter may last only five or ten *microseconds,* or millionths of a second. Most radar antennas turn around, sending pulses in each direction as they turn. When a pulse strikes an object, the object reflects the pulse back to the radar antenna (*see diagram*).

The reflected pulse goes to the radar receiver, where it is *amplified,* or strengthened, then sent to the *indicator,* or screen. The

This is what the blips look like
on a radar screen.
(RCA Radiomarine Photograph)

screen is the flat end of an electronic tube, which looks like a television tube. On the screen, a pulse reflected back from a ship or airplane, for example, shows up as a bright spot of light, called a *blip*. Blips on the operator's screen make up a miniature map of the surrounding area, with the center of the screen representing the radar set's position.

The distance to a blip from the center of the screen is set by the time it takes a pulse to go from the antenna to the object and back again. By measuring on the screen, the operator can learn, for example, that an airplane is 10 miles north of his position or a city is 25 miles southwest. He can also figure out the speed of moving objects. Other objects that show up well are large buildings, groups of buildings, railroad yards, and bridges.

Radar is used at airports to control air traffic and in airplanes for navigating and for avoiding storm clouds. Ships carry radar so they can detect other ships in fog. Special kinds of radar sets have bounced pulses off the Moon to measure its distance from the Earth. Scientists who study birds have also used radar to study the flight paths of birds as they migrate.

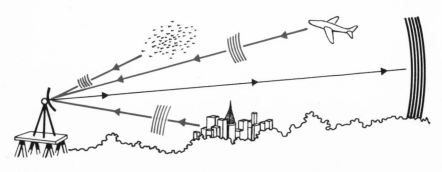

TRANSPORTATION

Automobiles, saws, power lawnmowers, motorcycles, generators, and countless other machines now are powered by gasoline, and the roar of the internal combustion engine is heard throughout the land. The internal combustion engine is almost 150 years old. W. Cecil reported experiments with such an engine before 1838, when William Barnett actually built a one-cylinder engine. By the time of the American Civil War, these engines were already used to operate machinery such as printing presses. In 1885, Daimler and Benz developed engines that were basically the same as the ones we use today.

GASOLINE ENGINE

A gasoline engine works something like a gun. In a gun, gunpowder explodes and gases from the explosion push a bullet out of the barrel. The "barrel" of an engine is called a *cylinder,* and it is about three inches in diameter. The "bullet" is called a *piston,* but the explosion moves it only to the end of the cylinder. And the "gunpowder" is a mixture of gasoline and air. Here is how a typical four-stroke gasoline engine works:

First, the piston slides downward in the cylinder, leaving a partial vacuum. Tiny droplets of gasoline that have been mixed with air are sucked into the cylinder through an open *intake valve.* This is called the *intake stroke (see diagram).*

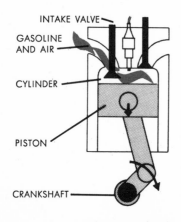

INTAKE STROKE   **COMPRESSION STROKE**

Next, the piston moves up in the cylinder and presses the gasoline-air mixture into a very small space. This is the *compression stroke*.

Then, a spark plug, in the top of the cylinder, makes an electrical spark that explodes the mixture of gasoline and air. The gases produced in this explosion push the piston downward. This is called the *power stroke*. A rod connects the piston to the *crankshaft*, making it turn as the piston moves down and up. The crankshaft turns gears that make the car wheels go around.

Finally, the *exhaust valve* opens and the piston moves upward, forcing the gases out of the cylinder. This is called the *exhaust stroke*.

Then the exhaust valve closes, the piston starts downward again, and more of the gasoline and air mixture is let in to start the four-stroke operation all over again. This operation takes place many times each minute in each cylinder of the engine.

The piston in each cylinder supplies power only on the power stroke. At other times, it is being moved up and down by the crankshaft as it is turned by the power strokes of other pistons. An automobile engine may have from four to twelve cylinders. The more cylinders it has, the more force it applies to turning the crankshaft.

There are other devices that help the engine do its work. The *carburetor* changes liquid gasoline into tiny droplets and mixes it with air, the same way a sprayer vaporizes perfume. A *battery* stores electricity and supplies it to the spark plugs. The *exhaust pipe* carries waste gases away from the engine.

The next time you see a car with the hood up, try to identify the engine parts you can see. How many cylinders does the car have? How can you tell?

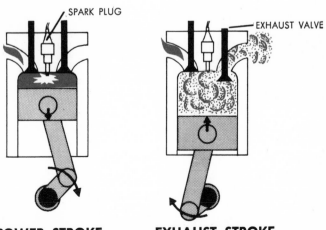

POWER STROKE   **EXHAUST STROKE**

It remained for Duryea, Ford, and other pioneers in the automobile business to put the nation on wheels by installing gasoline engines in buggies. But once you drove away from your home, where could you fill the gas tank? The answer was, obviously, a gasoline station, and thousands of them have appeared on the highways of the world. Technology has not been idle in the case of the development of the gas pump, either.

GASOLINE DISPENSER

"Fill 'er up!" When the gas station attendant hears this, he switches on the gasoline dispenser, sticks the hose nozzle into the opening of your car's tank, and presses a trigger that lets gasoline flow from the nozzle. If the nozzle has an automatic valve, the attendant can walk away to wash the windshield or check the engine oil, because the nozzle will turn itself off when the tank is filled. Here is how it works.

When the attendant switches on the dispenser, an electric motor turns the pump that brings gasoline from an underground storage tank to the dispenser (*see Diagram A*). But the dispenser is already filled with gasoline right up to the nozzle, so the fluid from the pump flows around a loop of pipe, back to the pump, until the nozzle is opened. Then, as gasoline flows out of the nozzle, the gasoline from the pump flows into the *air eliminator tank*.

Removing the Air

The gasoline carries some air bubbles from the storage tank, which has a *ventline,* or pipe that is open at the end above the ground. The ventline lets air escape from the tank as gasoline is pumped into it and lets air into the tank as the gasoline is pumped out of it. The air bubbles have to be removed so that you pay only for gasoline.

Since the air bubbles are lighter than the gasoline, they stay at the top of the eliminator tank and run off with a little gasoline into the *settling chamber* (*see diagram*). There the air escapes into the atmosphere and the gasoline flows back to the pump.

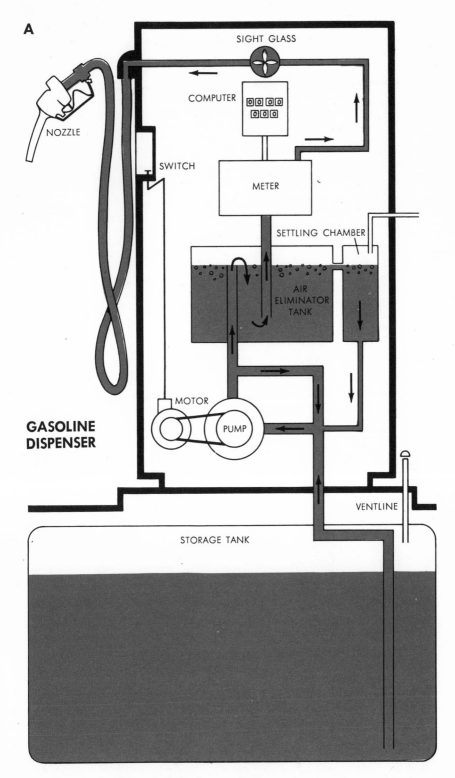

A

SIGHT GLASS

NOZZLE

COMPUTER

SWITCH

METER

SETTLING CHAMBER

AIR ELIMINATOR TANK

GASOLINE DISPENSER

MOTOR

PUMP

VENTLINE

STORAGE TANK

From the bottom of the air eliminator tank, the "purified" gaso-line flows up through a pipe to the *meter.* The gasoline is measured in two *cylinders,* or chambers, with *pistons* that move back and forth inside them to let gasoline in and push it out (*see Diagram B*). (Some meters have only one cylinder; others have up to five cylinders.) A rod connects each piston to the bent section of the

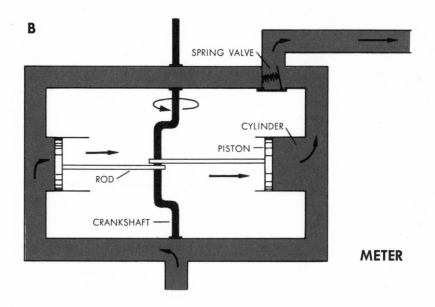

B

SPRING VALVE

CYLINDER

PISTON

ROD

CRANKSHAFT

METER

crankshaft, which can turn inside the ring at the end of each rod.

As gasoline flows into the left cylinder, it pushes the piston inward, making the rod push the crankshaft around one half turn. As the bend in the crankshaft moves around, it pushes the other piston outward. This pushes the gasoline out of the right cylinder, through one side of a *spring valve,* and out of the meter.

When the piston reaches the outside end of the right cylinder, it no longer pushes the gasoline, so the spring valve closes. Then the gasoline flows from the eliminator tank into the right cylinder. The piston is pushed inward, giving the crankshaft another half turn and pushing the gasoline out of the left cylinder and through the left side of the spring valve.

In this way, two cylindersful of gasoline give the crankshaft one complete turn. By means of gears, the crankshaft turns two rows of wheels in the *computer.* As the numbers around the edges of the wheels pass the windows in the dispenser, you can see how much gasoline has been pumped into your car and how much you have to pay for it.

Before the gasoline flows into the hose, it goes past the *sight glass*. This lets you see that the dispenser is full of gasoline right from the start, and a little paddle wheel turns when the gasoline is flowing into the hose.

An *automatic dispenser nozzle* stops the flow of gasoline when the car tank is full. When the trigger is pulled up and locked in place by the *spring clip*, it opens a valve and lets the gasoline flow out. It also pulls down the *latch plunger (see Diagram C)*. As the gasoline flows past the open end of a tube that leads to the *diaphragm chamber*, it draws air into the chamber through a narrow tube that runs from the chamber down through the nozzle. This tube is closed at the end, but has a tiny hole near the end beside a hole in the nozzle.

When the gasoline in the tank closes off this hole, it also presses back on the gasoline flowing through the nozzle. A little of this gasoline is pushed into the tube that leads to the diaphragm chamber. It *compresses*, or squeezes, the air trapped in there. This compressed air pushes down the rubber diaphragm and the *latch pin* connected to it. When the latch pin hits the latch plunger, it pushes the end of the trigger down just enough to release the other end of the trigger from the spring clip. The trigger springs down and closes the nozzle valve.

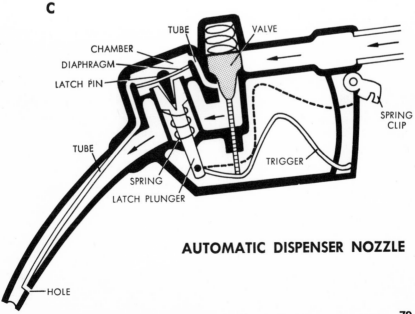

AUTOMATIC DISPENSER NOZZLE

As the automobile developed into a super-charged bullet capable of traveling at speeds of 60, 80, or 100 miles per hour, the speedometer became an essential item of equipment. It is a safety feature that reminds the driver of his speed so that he can use better judgment as he moves along the street or the highway.

SPEEDOMETER

You are riding in a car that moves six feet each time the wheels go around, and you know that the wheels are going around 440 times a minute. Can you figure out how fast the car is going in miles per hour?

You don't have to, of course, because the car's speedometer is a computer that shows you the speed of the car at each instant. Here is how it works.

A gear on the shaft that drives the car wheels turns another gear on the end of a steel cable (*see diagram*). As the shaft turns, the cable spins around inside a flexible metal casing. The cable runs through this casing to the back of the speedometer. There, the end of the cable is attached to an ordinary bar magnet so that the magnet spins around whenever the car wheels are turning.

The magnet is inside an aluminum cup, and a thin shaft connects the cup to the *pointer* (*see diagram*). A coil spring holds the cup and shaft so that the pointer is at 0 on the speedometer dial when the car is stopped. But when its wheels turn, the magnet begins to spin, and the cup turns a fraction of an inch or so in the same direction as the magnet. This moves the pointer to, say, 10 on the speedometer dial. The faster the magnet spins, the farther the cup turns. But when the magnet slows down, the cup turns back in the opposite direction, moving the pointer to a lower number on the speedometer dial.

Since a magnet does not attract aluminum, and the bar magnet does not touch the cup, you may wonder what makes the cup

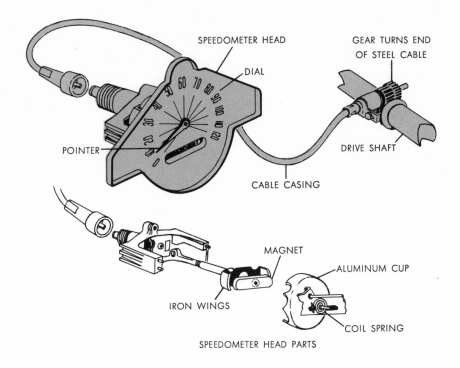

SPEEDOMETER HEAD

GEAR TURNS END
OF STEEL CABLE

DIAL

POINTER

DRIVE SHAFT

CABLE CASING

MAGNET

ALUMINUM CUP

IRON WINGS

COIL SPRING

SPEEDOMETER HEAD PARTS

move. Aluminum, like all other substances, has tiny particles in it called *electrons*. These electrons are moved around inside the aluminum by the pull of the spinning bar magnet. This movement of electrons is an *electric current*. And this current makes the cup act like a magnet, even though it is aluminum.

Two iron wings are attached to the bar magnet so they whirl around the cup as the bar magnet spins inside it (*see diagram*). Because of the pull between the iron wings and the "magnetized" cup, the cup is dragged in the direction the wings are whirling, but the coil spring keeps the cup from turning very far. As the bar magnet spins faster, the current in the cup grows stronger, and the cup turns farther. When the magnet slows down, the current gets weaker, so the cup and pointer are pulled backward by the coil spring.

In this way, the speedometer uses an electric current to "imitate" the turning of the car wheels and thus compute how fast the car is moving at each instant. "Imitating" devices are also used to keep track of the speed and direction of airplanes and ships. Others are used in laboratories and factories to measure such things as how fast a liquid is flowing or how hard a press is pressing.

Almost all brakes operate on the basis of applied friction—some immovable object being pressed against a part of the wheel to slow it down. There are many kinds of these devices, from the mechanical brakes used on wagons and the earliest automobiles, to the hydraulic brakes used on automobiles today and the air brakes of heavy trucks and railroad trains. There are even brakes powered by electricity.

BRAKES

What happens when you "jam on your brakes" when you're running fast? You stop, of course. But what makes you stop?

When your shoes plow up the ground or scrape against the hard surface of a playground, *friction* slows you down. Whenever two surfaces rub against each other, friction slows down the moving objects. For example, friction with the air slows down a baseball or a football. The greater the friction, or rubbing, the greater the braking power. Why is it harder to walk on ice than on the pavement?

Automobiles, railroad cars, and your bicycle all have brakes that produce friction by making part of a wheel rub against a different object. When someone works the brakes, he pushes the two surfaces together and the wheel stops.

Here is how one kind of **bicycle brake** works. Around the rear axle is a metal cylinder called the *brake drum,* which turns with the wheel (*see diagram*). When you push backward on a pedal, you cause two *brake shoes* to push against the inside surface of the brake drum. This produces friction and the wheel either slows down or stops, depending on how hard you push on the pedal.

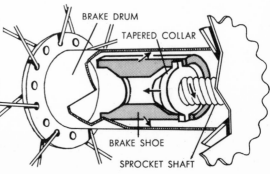

Pushing your bicycle pedal backward turns the rear wheel sprocket and unscrews the tapered collar from a sprocket shaft. The collar moves between the brake shoes (only one is shown) and forces them outward against the brake drum.

BRAKE DRUM
TAPERED COLLAR
BRAKE SHOE
SPROCKET SHAFT

Here is how one kind of **automobile brake** works. The brake pedal pushes a piston into a cylinder filled with oil. This increases pressure on the oil. An oil-filled tube runs from this cylinder to another one near a wheel (*see diagram*). The increase in pressure on the oil in the first cylinder is passed along to the oil in the tube and to the oil in the second cylinder. The pressure in the second cylinder moves two pistons attached to brake shoes. The shoes press against a turning brake drum on the wheel. Friction between the brake shoes and brake drum slows or stops the wheel. This is a *hydraulic* brake system; it depends on the pressure of liquid to move parts.

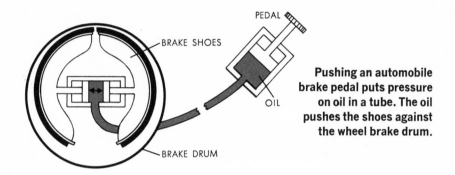

Pushing an automobile brake pedal puts pressure on oil in a tube. The oil pushes the shoes against the wheel brake drum.

Railroad car brakes, like the "hissing" brakes on buses and large trucks, are operated by air pressure, rather than oil pressure. An increase in air pressure in the tubes and cylinders of the system pushes the brake shoes against the moving surface of the wheel itself (*see diagram*).

What kind of brakes does your family car have? What kind of brakes does your bicycle have? Do hand brakes on a bicycle work like hydraulic brakes?

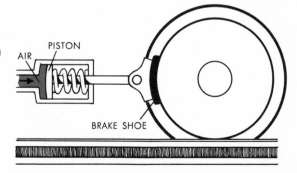

Compressed air enters a railroad brake cylinder and pushes a piston, which pushes brake shoe against a wheel.

PHOTOGRAPHY

Almost half of the families in the United States own at least one camera. But few members of these families realize that the camera was invented during the sixteenth century. This was the camera obscura, *which some historians say was invented by Leonardo da Vinci. It was a box, larger than a man, with a tiny hole in one end to let in light. This light then formed an image on the opposite wall. Bulky as it was, it was quite similar to the design of some of our simpler modern cameras.*

CAMERA

Cameras work in much the same way that your eye does. Like your eye, a camera is a light-tight box with an opening and lens at the front and film at the back. Your eye also has a lens at the front and a "film" at the back (*see diagrams*).

Suppose that you are looking at an aardvark and want to photograph it. Light reflected from the animal enters the lens of your eye and the lens of your camera. As the light enters the lenses, it is *refracted,* or bent and forms an image. In your eye the image is projected on the back wall, called the *retina.* In a camera the image is projected onto the film. You can think of your retina as a special kind of "film."

Cameras other than simple box cameras have several devices that help you control the brightness and sharpness of the image

HUMAN EYE

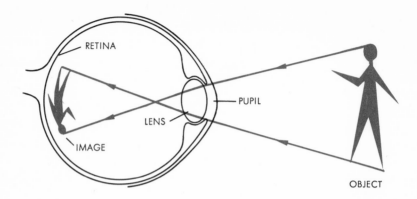

projected onto the film. One of these is called a *diaphragm*. It is a circular opening that you can make large or small. If you allow too much light to strike the film by opening the diaphragm too wide, your picture will be overexposed and will look faint. If you set the diaphragm opening too small, you underexpose the picture and it comes out dark.

Our eye's "diaphragm opening" is called the *pupil*. Muscles in the eye automatically adjust the size of the pupil so that just the right amount of light enters the eye. You have probably seen the pupils of a cat's eyes change size.

A camera also controls the amount of light striking the film by means of the *shutter*. The longer the shutter stays open, the more light falls on the film. By leaving the shutter open too long you can overexpose a picture; and by leaving it open too short a time,

SIMPLE CAMERA

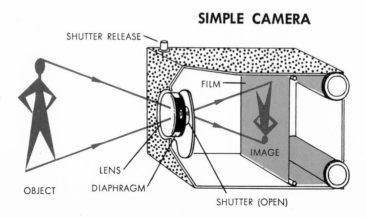

you underexpose the picture. In a sense, our eyelids are shutters. By closing them we cut out all light entering our eyes.

When you take a photograph, you press the button called the *shutter release*. In a split second the shutter flicks open and closes again. During the instant it is open, light rays from the object you are photographing strike the film and cause a chemical change on the film. When the film is developed another chemical change takes place. You see this chemical change as the film negative.

You have probably noticed some pictures that come out all fuzzy, or out of focus. When a photograph is fuzzy, it is because the camera lens was not adjusted properly. It was either too far away or too close to the film. Some cameras have a window of ground glass that you can look through and see the object that you want to photograph.

When we look at an object we do not have to think about bringing it into focus. The eye muscles do this for us automatically. When we look at an object far away, our eye muscles tend to make the lenses of your eyes slightly flattened. When we look at an object close up, the muscles shorten the eyeball, making the lens bulge out slightly.

The shape of a camera lens cannot be changed, so we produce a sharp image by moving the lens closer to or farther away from the film.

The lens of a camera and the lens of an eye both produce an upside-down image (*see diagrams*). In a photograph we can correct this simply by turning the picture around when we look at it. It is the brain that turns the upside-down image on our retina to a right-side-up position.

When photographic film was invented, photography came into its own. No longer would an artist have to trace the image in a camera obscura. In the early 1800s, experimenters used a light-sensitive metal plate, which was then engraved to keep the image. In the 1800s, Daguerre invented his daguerreotype, a refinement of the metal plate process.· From 1839, when light-sensitive paper came into being, until the present, new developments have come thick and fast in the making of photographic film.

PHOTOGRAPHIC FILM

When you take a picture, you let light into your camera for a fraction of a second. This light forms an image in the back of the camera which is a tiny, upside-down picture of whatever is in front of the camera. The image falls on the film which is in the back of your camera.

The film has a coating of chemicals that contain silver. In the places where the image in the camera is bright, a lot of light hits the film. In those places, tiny grains of pure silver are formed on the film. You can't see these grains unless you use a microscope, but where there are a lot of them together they make the film black. Where the image is dark, not much light hits the film. In those places few grains of silver are formed, so the film is gray or even lighter (*see Diagram 1*).

When the film is *developed,* the chemicals that were not exposed to light are washed away. After that, light will not change the film any more. The tiny grains of silver remain on the film in the places that were exposed to light. This developed film is

1

IMAGE IN
CAMERA

NEGATIVE IMAGE
ON FILM

called a *negative,* because its light and dark areas are just the reverse of the image in the camera.

To make a *positive,* or picture just like the image in the camera, light is sent through the negative onto a piece of paper that is coated with the same sort of chemicals as the film. The paper is then developed. Where the negative is dark the positive will be light, like the original image.

How Color Film Works

Color film works the same way as black-and-white film. Color pictures are not really recorded in color. The colors you see when you look at a color slide come from dyes that are put into the film when it is developed. A color film is really three black-and-white films put together like a sandwich (*see Diagram 2A*). Each of these films records light of a different color. In the top layer silver is formed only by blue light; the middle layer is sensitive to green light, and the bottom layer to red light. All the other colors of light can be made by mixing light of these three colors in different proportions.

Some color films are developed into negatives and used to make color prints, but most color films are developed in a different way to make positive slides. The film layers are dyed different colors. The top layer is dyed yellow, the middle layer purple, and the bottom layer blue-green. These dyes are dark where the original image in the camera was dark, and light where the image was light.

For example, in a place where the image in the camera was blue—like the sky in an outdoor picture—the top layer of film has little or no yellow dye. When you look through the slide at a white light, the blue-green and purple layers stop, or *filter out,* all of the colors of light except blue. So that part of the film will look blue. All the other colors are made in the same way—by filtering out some colors from the white light (*see Diagram 2B*).

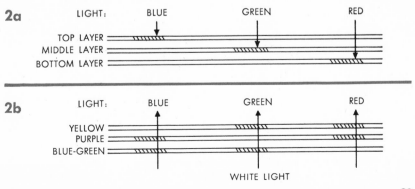

Once the photograph is made, how can it be printed in a book or a newspaper? During the Civil War there were many photographers, but no way had been perfected to reproduce their photographs clearly by using a printing press. Although the photoengraving process had been developed in 1852, it was not until 1890 that the halftone process came into general use.

PRINTED PHOTOGRAPHS

Photographs that are not printed in color are actually many different shades of gray. But a printing press can't print gray with black ink—it either prints black or it doesn't print at all.

Look at a newspaper photograph with a magnifying glass. You will see that the photograph is made up of thousands of tiny black dots (*see illustration*). When you see the picture without a magnifying glass, the mixture of dots and white spaces appear to be different shades of gray.

A picture that is to be printed must first be broken up into a pattern of dots. To do this, a photograph of the picture is taken through a piece of glass with thousands of criss-crossed lines on it (*see illustration*). This is called a *halftone screen*. (You can see how it works by looking through a window screen with your eyes about two inches from the screen.)

When the film is developed, the image you see is made up of tiny dots because light from the picture passed through the half-tone screen on its way to the film.

The film is laid on a sheet of metal (usually copper, zinc or magnesium) that has a special coating on it, and then exposed to a strong light. The light shines through the light spots of the film and hardens the coating on the metal sheet, or *plate,* where the light is not blocked by dark areas on the film.

Washing the plate removes the soft parts of the coating that were not exposed to light. This leaves the metal bare at those points. The plate is then put in a tank with acid that eats away, or *etches,* some of the bare metal and leaves tiny, flat-topped mountains of coated metal (*see illustration*). The process of making a halftone plate is called *photoengraving*.

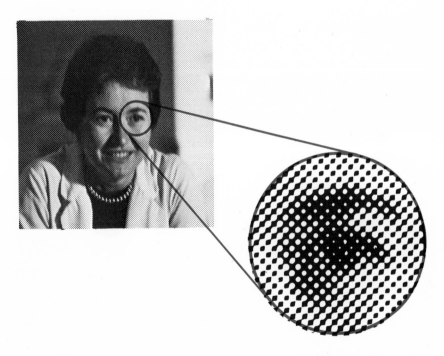

This enlarged section of a newspaper photograph shows that the light areas are made of tiny black dots surrounded by white space. Dark areas are made of larger dots that leave almost no white space. There are 4,225 dots per square inch in this photograph. Compare it with other photographs in this book, which have 14,400 dots per square inch.

When the plate is put on the printing press, a roller spreads ink over the flat tops of the mountains. No ink goes into the valleys between them. A sheet of white paper is pressed against the plate, and picks up the ink in the form of tiny black dots. The patterns of black dots against the white paper produce areas that range from light gray to black in the printed photograph. Printed color photographs are mixtures of red, yellow, blue, and black dots printed from four separate halftone plates.

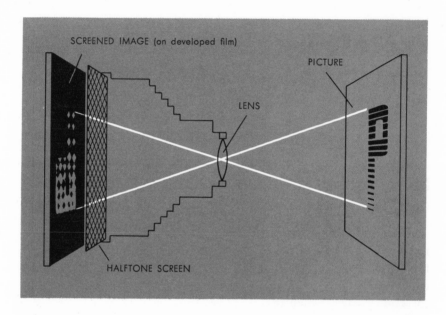

SCREENED IMAGE (on developed film)

PICTURE

LENS

HALFTONE SCREEN

The picture to be printed is first photographed through a glass screen that is criss-crossed by many lines. Light from the picture goes through the tiny "holes" in the screen and forms an image of the picture in dots on the film.

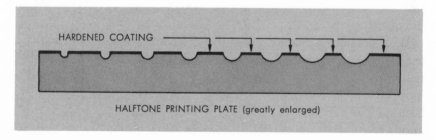

HARDENED COATING

HALFTONE PRINTING PLATE (greatly enlarged)

Next the film is laid on a coated metal plate and exposed to light. Where light goes through dot "holes" in the film, it hardens dots of coating on the plate. The unhardened coating is washed off, leaving bare metal around the dots. The acid eats out the metal between the dots to leave flat-topped "mountains" that print black dots of ink.

The basic principle of the motion picture—persistence of vision—was discovered before the Christian Era, and over the centuries scientists developed countless ways of producing pictures that appeared to move. But it wasn't until George Eastman invented flexible film (long after the discovery of popcorn) that it was possible to show motion pictures as we know them. And in 1896, Thomas Edison was the first to project a motion picture on a screen.

MOVING PICTURES

The pictures you see on a movie screen show people and things moving as they do in real life. But if you look at a strip of movie film, you will find it is made up of many little "still" pictures, called *frames* (*see photo*). What makes these still pictures seem to "come to life" when they are shown through a movie projector?

The frames next to each other on a strip of movie film seem almost alike. But if you look closely at the frames of movie film shown on this page, you can see that the donkey's legs are in slightly different places in each frame. These pictures were taken just one-sixteenth of a second apart as the donkey walked along the street.

With a snapshot camera, you could take a single still picture of the donkey at any instant in his walk. But by the time you were ready to take another picture, the donkey would have taken several more steps. A home movie camera has a wind-up spring, or a battery-driven electric motor, that makes it take one picture after another. It takes 16 separate pictures each second!

When you press the trigger of a movie camera, the spring or motor pulls a "fresh," or *unexposed,* part of the film into place behind the lens. When the film stops moving, the shutter opens to let the light coming through the lens strike the film. Then the shutter closes and the film is moved again. (The shutter is a metal disc with holes around the edge. It turns just fast enough to let light reach the film only when the film is not moving.) The pictures are taken so rapidly that they show the donkey's legs in several different positions during each step.

After all of the film has run through the camera, it is taken out and developed.

When you see a movie film projected on a screen, your eye seems to see motion. But here is what actually happens: A very bright bulb shines light through the film and out the lens to a screen. The film moves through the projector in 16 quick jumps each second, so that one frame is flashed on the screen at a time. A shutter like the one in a movie camera blocks out the light while the film is moving. If the projector ran slow enough, you could see the screen go black between frames. Because the projector shows the pictures one after another in such quick jumps, your eyes don't see the black between frames. And to your eyes, the slight movement of the donkey's legs from one frame to the next becomes a smooth, "real life" step.

INDEX

Dr. Thomas G. Aylesworth has been involved with science teaching and science projects for many years. He taught junior and senior high school science and graduate and undergraduate courses in science education at the university level. Besides teaching, Dr. Aylesworth has served as head of a science department, has conducted National Science Foundation institutes and science education workshops, and was formerly senior editor of a nationally circulated weekly junior high school science newspaper.

At present he is a senior editor for a major publisher and lives in Connecticut with his wife, two children, and a cat.